THE OTHER JACK

Charles Boyle was born in 1951. He has published poetry, fiction and non-fiction under his own name and two pen names. In 2007 he founded the small press CB editions.

by the same author

CHARLES BOYLE
Paleface
The Age of Cardboard and String
The Disguise: Poems 1977–2001
The Manet Girl

JENNIE WALKER
24 for 3

JACK ROBINSON
Recessional
Days and Nights in W12
Robinson
An Overcoat: Scenes from the Afterlife of H.B.
Good Morning, Mr Crusoe
Blush (with Natalia Zagórska-Thomas)

The Other Jack

A book about books, mostly

Charles Boyle

First published in 2021
by CB editions
146 Percy Road, London W12 9QL
www.cbeditions.com

Lines by Rosemary Tonks quoted on page 120 are from
Bedouin of the London Evening: Collected Poems (Bloodaxe, 2014),
reproduced with permission of Bloodaxe Books

Printed in England by Blissetts, London W3 8DH

ISBN 978-1-909585-41-6

'Don't they ask your name?'

'Yep.'

'What do you call yourself?'

'Oh, Jackson or anything.' He flicks a glance at me. We begin to laugh, looking away from each other.

– Helen Garner, 'Postcards from Surfers'

Life is an anti-novel.

– Elizabeth Bowen, *Eva Trout*

One	1
Two	47
Three	104
Four	148
References	177
Index	181

I 've replied to Robyn's email. I explained about Jack, and I mentioned Jennie too. I didn't mention the bed scene I'm pretty sure I *didn't* write. So now she knows who I am, roughly. We are going to meet. Bookish blather in a bistro – what can go wrong?

Rewind. Someone was running, hard, behind me. Had I paid for my coffee? 'Stop thief!' people used to shout in the speech bubbles in cartoons. I'd walked off without paying, and the footsteps were those of the waiter chasing after me. I blushed and turned and she almost knocked me over. Grinning, out of breath, she handed me a book I had left on the café table. Had I read *Recessional*, she asked, by the same author? No, I said, not that one, although in fact I have read it. In fact I wrote it. But she seemed a little *eager*. She was young – younger than my children – and it was starting to rain and neither of us had an umbrella. You should, she said. It's one of the early ones but it's still his best.

Jack Robinson wrote *Recessional*, a slim book about the 2008 financial crash, and the book I had been reading in the café and some others too, and I was Jack. People usually prefer a joke or a song or a story to an explanation, but here goes. In 2007 I published four books under an imprint I made up on a whim and two of them were by me. I planned to take copies of the books into local bookshops and humbly suggest they might like to stock them. If I was lucky, the bookseller would look warily at the books and say, 'Tell me about the authors.' This wasn't going to work. In a bookseller's book, self-published authors are shady characters. They can come across as a little desperate – with reason, but it's not a good look. So, Jack Robinson. (And also Jennie Walker, but one at a time.) Will that do? Probably not. Pen names are a form of dissembling and cannot be fobbed off with an anecdote about Jack. More about this later. Trust me. (This is the basic contract between writer and reader, and it has to be signed during the first few pages and here we are. The reader is free to cancel at any point.) For the moment, just this: the pen names of dead authors are taken as read but if the author is alive people worry. There's a whiff of forgery. Someone is pulling a fast one. The author has something to hide. The author is setting up an alibi in case it all goes horribly wrong.

Explanation and instruction are undervalued uses of language. It's more fun to shop for scallops than for toilet rolls and cat food. But we do often need to be told how things work or fit together, and if we are not told very clearly then a lot of damage can result. My French teacher in the 1960s asked me to describe a spiral staircase without using my hands. That was excellent teaching.

There's an expression on people's faces that says: I don't get it, I think I'm missing something here. Sometimes they are right, enough information hasn't been given. Other times, that's all there is.

Being a writer *without* a pen name can attract suspicion. In *Ways of Going Home*, Alejandro Zambra tells of a woman who, learning that he was writer – a writer of 'action novels': 'it isn't exactly a lie, since in all novels, even mine, things happen' – asked what his pseudonym was. He told her he didn't have one. The woman 'looked at me skeptically . . . When we said goodbye she told me not to worry, maybe soon I would come up with a good pseudonym.' I haven't met her, this woman with a healthy distrust of writers, but I think she was disappointed in the powers of invention of a man whose job was to make people up.

Lisbon, summer 2019. The last time I was here was 35 years ago, when most of the people who live here now were not yet born. I walk to the vast Praça do Comércio with the equestrian statue of King José I plumped in its middle – snakes writhing under José's horse, elephants on the plinth – because this is where the protagonist of a novel that I've been reading used to stand, facing the Tagus, worrying about the mess he's made of his life, so you could say that my walking to the square is a form of pilgrimage, though really that's no more than saying it's tourism with a literary sun hat on. I bought the book after reading a review by a writer whose recommendations I follow up, and I was left with a sense of disappointment – not so much with Antonio Muñoz Molina's novel as with the writer whose say-so had set up such high expectations; or rather, with myself for having assumed that just because I once believed this writer was a god he would always be infallible. That's too much to ask, even of gods. The protagonist of Molina's novel is James Earl Ray, the killer of Martin Luther King. On the run – 'perfecting his ability to leave no strong impression on others, so that they can only remember him in the most generalised ways' – he lives for a while in a cheap hotel in Lisbon under an assumed name while attempting to acquire a visa to travel to Angola. Other people besides fugitives from justice (and writers) who may choose to live or work under names other than those they were given at birth: terrorists, spies, conmen and hackers, converts to certain religions and cults, false claimants to inheritance or to the thrones of minor principalities, undercover police agents infiltrating animal rights groups, actors in porn films, earls and dukes and sundry other peers of the realm, money launderers, former Nazis in hiding, right-wing activists, drug dealers and trolls on Twitter. And most wives. The rich stash cash in offshore accounts held in the name of shell companies. Lisbon's most celebrated writer, Fernando Pessoa, whose poems you can buy in the tourist shops on tiles and tea towels, wrote under several pen names, which in his case are usually called heteronyms (there's a specialist vocab even for wandering around incognito) – the names here being masks for distinctively different writers, each with their own biography and personality.

The covers of the English-language editions of Eduardo Halfon's novels – or short-story collections or memoirs or books of auto-fiction – show wispy drifts of cigarette smoke with the titles in a matching smoky font. The narrator of these books, Eduardo Halfon – but some of the people he encounters choose to call him Hoffman – smokes a lot of cigarettes, of many different brands. 'I took out a cigarette and lit it, and the sweetish smoke began restoring my faith, a least a little, at least until I looked up and discovered that there before me, standing motionless in the distance on the asphalt road, was a horse.' Or: 'I lit the cigarette, my hand trembling, or perhaps it wasn't.' The smoking of cigarettes is structural to the narration: it offers pauses for reflection or an excuse to ask strangers for a light or temporary withdrawal from a tricky situation, or just something for the narrator to do while he's waiting for a taxi or is tired but not yet ready to sleep. It's repetitive because smoking *is* repetitive: one cigarette is invariably followed by another. All the secondary activity is in there: buying cigarettes from a corner shop or a vending machine, stripping the cellophane off the packet, looking around for an ashtray. Smoking is integral to the text – it's as if the horse appears on the asphalt road *because of* the cigarette. Meanwhile, the writer Eduardo Halfon gets invited to conferences and to give lectures, and has remarked in interview that 'everywhere I go they've always reserved for me a smoking room'. The writer Eduardo Halfon does not smoke.

There was a period in my life when the price of a pack of twenty cigarettes stayed roughly on a par with the price of a paperback novel, and now the world is out of joint.

I once fantasised about hitch-hiking across America and walking up the garden path and knocking on the door of the author I was dizzy about at the time. I wouldn't do it now. I might not like her. I can't think why she should like me. The consensus view of who any particular writer is, or was, as a person is often both wide of the mark and hard to shift. Kafka's biographer Reiner Stach noted that 'decades of international, interdisciplinary research . . . hardly seem to have made any impression on the popular imagination, where Kafka has persisted as the quintessential archetype of the writer as a sort of alien: unworldly, neurotic, introverted, sick – an uncanny man bringing forth uncanny things.' As a guide to what 'literary fiction' is too, or contemporary poetry or art, or 'immigrants' or 'the young' or even 'the old', the popular imagination is not a reliable source of information.

Imagine knocking on Kafka's door. And after half a minute, knocking again, a bit louder. Imagine peering through the letter flap – which Kafka's door almost certainly didn't have – to see what you can see. Hearing footsteps coming down the stairs but no, you're just imagining them. Knocking again, careful not make those knocks sound aggressive, you're not a bailiff, and deciding to wait until ten cars have passed by in the street before giving up and heading home. By the fifth car it has started to rain. You don't have an umbrella. After the tenth car has gone by and Kafka still hasn't materialised, do you (a) quit, go home; or (b) start counting again from one?

Rain again, the kind of low-level but persistent rain the Scots call a *smirr*. If the waitress thought that early book was Jack's best, then I have been a disappointment to her ever since.

Social awkwardness is more interesting than social ease, but on the day when the waitress chased after me I took a pass. In one of his memoirs Stendhal recalls that 'quite often in society' a stranger would congratulate him on his writing: 'The compliment and my reply done with, we didn't know what to say to each other.' Some silences are just waiting to be framed and hung on the wall. Some silences are a box I'm carrying around and can't find anywhere to put down. Both Stendhal and his admirer are in need of the waiter who is dipping in and out with open bottles, refilling glasses, the waiter on the minimum wage and a zero-hours contract.

Once, just slightly drunk, I congratulated an author on a book that he hadn't written. He did look like the actual author. He was confused but forgiving. He may even have thought that it was *his* mistake.

And then again. With a glass of book-party wine in my hand I was talking with A, a semi-famous writer – or maybe he was a publisher or reviewer or an organiser of festivals – when my friend B approached, clearly hoping that I would introduce him to A. I didn't. A few hours later, B emailed me: 'Fuck you.' I explained to B that the reason I didn't make the introduction was that I'd forgotten A's name, and I couldn't just make one up; god knows whether he believed me. No, the reason I didn't make the introduction was that A would assume that I wasn't interested in him enough to remember who he was. I had to decide, on the spot, which of the two of them would find me arrogant and stupid, and I chose, because of the semi-fame of A, wrong.

Someone else who told me to fuck off was a man in a wheelchair in the middle of the road in Fulham Broadway (he was holding up the traffic, and I'd offered to wheel him to the pavement). Also in Fulham Broadway I saw a man with a boa constrictor around his neck (he was taking it to the vet). There was a shop in Fulham Broadway where you could buy *anything* and which was destroyed by fire in 'mysterious circumstances'. It was while I was living around there in the late 1970s that for a period of several weeks or maybe months I believed that the world was about to end; I was not clinically depressed but to the me then there was no possibility of the me now, writing this.

'Then everything went black.' That line is a regular end-of-chapter cliffhanger in crime fiction. At the start of the next chapter, gumshoe regains consciousness with a sore head in an unfriendly place. The gumshoe gets beaten up and also chased around the block, spat on and lied to. He seems to invite this. The gumshoe is a guy – traditionally a guy – to whom things happen, rather than one who makes things happen. He doesn't *do* very much. He slouches. He drinks good whisky. He spends a lot of time sitting down. Women come on to him, which is part of the overall mystery. He watches, listens, tries to tease out patterns of motivation from chaos, and has the occasional lucky break. Writer as gumshoe.

In the top drawer of the gumshoe's desk there's often a gun. Lightweight and not large – sort of happy-to-see-you size. But I'm not going to put one there because of Chekhov's rule that if you put a gun in the first chapter then in a later chapter that gun has to be fired. It's a rule that can be broken – it may be enough to know that a gun is there, tucked behind the ear for later – but adding in a gun without having any intention of using it is a tease, so no gun.

The waitress emailed me: 'I'm the person who chased after you with your book', etc. She isn't really a waitress. The only real waiters are the ones past retirement age; the others are actors or singers or photographers or film-makers. They are rarely bankers. This one is a writer, or wants to *become* a writer, but meanwhile she has to feed herself and a waiter is only one letter different from a writer. She told me her name and she reminded me of a scene she is fond of in one of Jack's early books where the wife is masturbating and her husband is lying beside her in bed, reading, and the book he is reading is titled *Slow Mercy*. They are staying in a five-star hotel, the kind with a pool and a gym and over-egged flower arrangements in the lobby, and perhaps they've gone there to try to *patch up* their marriage, Robyn can't remember, but the book the husband is reading in bed must be a good book because he is taking a long time before turning each page, but then he starts skipping and the wife is distracted by this. At the time, and still now, that book didn't exist but at some point, Robyn thinks, Jack will get around to writing it. Otherwise why mention its title? I do sometimes forget what I have written but I have never written the scene that Robyn described, the wife masturbating while the husband is reading. She is confusing Jack with someone else. But technically it would be an interesting scene to write.

The reviewer on whose say-so I read the Lisbon novel was Michael Hofmann. As a child with German-speaking parents he moved between Germany, England, America and Scotland, eventually acquiring – as he put it in a 1999 interview – 'a kind of almost parodic Englishness'. Hofmann is a serial translator into English of books written in German, scores of them, writing in the service of others. Asked in that interview about his 'sense of identity', he suggested that it was precisely because of the 'errancy' of his formative years and the pressures from within and without (and the 'intolerable mismatch between them') that 'I have an overwhelmingly strong sense of who I am. After all, what else is there to hang on to, or to offer the reader?' I am straightforwardly English, monoglot, and had a settled childhood, yet for most of my life have had a weak sense of identity – because, I now think, no one questioned it, so it was assumed rather than consciously articulated, more a pre-scripted role than an identity. A luggage label. Think of me as the other Jack. Or one of many other Jacks (they are legion). These are interesting times for white, male, straight, middle-class English writers who had settled childhoods, because questions *are* being asked: Who do I think I am? Or: Who cares who I think I am?

Spoiler. The world is not going to be changed by a chat about books. An anecdote, a joke, a small confession, are all that's expected from 'in conversation' events with writers. They are reinforcements of troops that are already in position. In the West, and perhaps in the UK especially, writing and reading take place in a culture of rainy days and diminished expectations. The table talk of two other literary types is recorded in Louis Malle's film *My Dinner with Andre*, in which Wallace Shawn and Andre Gregory play 'fictionalised versions of themselves', as Wikipedia has it, having dinner in an upmarket New York restaurant. They are close friends and both work in the theatre, but in very different traditions (think Philip Larkin having dinner with Velimir Khlebnikov). Gregory has worked in a forest in Poland with Jerzy Grotowski and also in Findhorn in Scotland and in India, Tibet and the Sahara. He speaks of wildness and tenderness and transformation. Shawn walks to the restaurant in a shabby coat with a missing button, remembering when he was young and 'all I thought about was art and music' – now he is 36 and 'all I think about is money'. But far from being disappointed with his lot, he relishes it. He carries out 'errands and responsibilities' and crosses them off the list in his notebook; he is happy when he gets up in the morning and there's no dead cockroach in his coffee cup; and he tells Gregory that he 'cannot imagine how anyone could enjoy something else any more than that'. He reads, he goes to parties with his girlfriend, and 'Occasionally if I can get my little talent together and write a little play, that's just wonderful . . . I enjoy reading other little plays people have written, and reading reviews about these plays, and what people have said about them, and what people said about what people said.' The ancient white-haired maître d' in the restaurant is a stand-in for God, his face lined by decades of pouring fine wines and breathing in cigar smoke and observing what a fuck-up we have made of free will, nodding gravely but without comment as we choose from the menu.

Auden: 'Poetry makes nothing happen.' When did poets stop claiming to be unacknowledged legislators and literature that it could at least be of some redemptive value? They stopped when their claims became hard to distinguish from company mission statements or inspirational quotes in fancy fonts posted on Facebook. Capitalism thrives on this: buying in the avant-garde manifestos and reselling them as lifestyle. Poetry can speak truth to power but power doesn't have to listen and very rarely chooses to do so; or listens but decides, for obvious reasons, it doesn't have to *do* anything about it. What's troubling about Auden's 'Poetry makes nothing happen' is its complacency. For Auden himself, poetry made a lot happen: Faber, America, Oxford, fame, prestige.

There is little here about violence, or love, or history and betrayal. I worry about fonts and design and umbrellas. And whether the number of lines on a page is divisible by three. It didn't start this way. In my late teens I was reading for life, the life I wasn't living but which was out there, surely. The writers who meant most to me were D. H. Lawrence and

David Storey: both northern, both sons of miners, neither on any syllabus. At university I 'read', as they say, English Lit, and the critical work that went with that – 'humanist', in that pre-critical theory age – was a form of elevated shop talk. Some of it was glorious; all of it was written in book-lined studies by serious white men who smoked pipes.

Robyn arrived on her bike. Resting on a spare chair at our table, her cycling helmet looked like a robot's ear or a low-tech 1970s recording device. She had brought her copy of *Recessional* for me sign for her and, Bartleby-ish, I told her that I would prefer not to. Do I sign as Jack or as me? Both names? On the flyleaf of the book there was already an inscription: 'For Robyn, love of my life, E.' How to follow that? Quite enough names there already. The book had been a present from a boyfriend on his birthday: birthdays, for him, were for giving, not receiving. She didn't get round to reading it until after they had split up – he took a job in New York, flew off – and she says it changed the way she thought about him. Not completely, but it put a different light on their relationship. She read it one afternoon in Manchester, sitting on a park bench, it's only 60 pages long, and while she was reading it the book became, in a way, *him*, her ex-boyfriend, though it was an unlikely substitute. Jack Robinson and the boyfriend had nothing in common. They wouldn't know what to say to each other if they met. They might look at each other's shoes. Maybe he thought *she* was like Jack? And while Robyn was telling me about Manchester I was thinking, the reason she thinks *Recessional* is Jack's best book is because she is still in love with her ex-boyfriend.

She was wearing a Ted Baker T-shirt. The young dress more smartly than they did when I was Robyn's age; and there are more homeless people on the streets. I knew it was a Ted Baker because she was wearing it inside out and there was the label under the collar on the back. Robyn: It's metafiction, innit? The seams were showing. Metafiction is big and Robyn has taken to wearing her clothes inside out. Most people assume she just got dressed in a hurry but no, it isn't an accident, she's put some thought into this. Exposing the artificiality of conventions involves even more artifice than was originally required. Metafiction has been around since long before me, Robyn or Ted Baker.

Growing up, Robyn and I read from very different menus. In late 1963, aged twelve, I made a list of books I had read in that year. Just two out of the forty titles on the list – which I lost for a while because I had put it in a safe place – were by women and only one was specifically written for children. All the authors were white. The authors with two or more titles on the list were C. S. Forester, John Buchan, Conan Doyle, Jack London, H. G. Wells and Rider Haggard. Writers still alive in 1963 included Hammond Innes and Alistair MacLean. This was high-protein fuel (Randall Jarrell claimed that in childhood he used to read half his weight in a week). It was also a typical mid-20th-century white boy's list: war and animals, mostly. Empire was deeply engrained. The library at the boys' boarding school where I was reading these books resembled a London gentlemen's club: leather armchairs and copies of *Punch* and the *Illustrated London News* in leather-bound folders on a mahogany table kept to a high polish by the school maids. By the time Robyn began reading, Young Adults had been invented, and she was offered a much wider range of subject matter – drugs, sex, family break-up – by a much wider range of writers. I don't know how our contrasting early reading conditioned our later reading lives, but they must have made *some* difference.

Pause, briefly, at leather: armchairs, belts and straps, car-seat upholstery, luggage, shoes, book bindings . . . We'll get to umbrellas later. In the period when I was being taught how to grow up – taught on the whole very badly, at great expense – leather was a marker of English class and masculinity, a demonstration of the hunter's superiority over his prey. Early in Ford Madox Ford's *The Good Soldier* (1915), the American narrator is bemused by Captain Edward Ashburnham's abundance of leather cases – 'all of pigskin and stamped with his initials, E.F.A. There were gun cases, and collar cases, and shirt cases, and letter cases and cases each containing four bottles of medicine; and hat cases and helmet cases. It must have needed a whole herd of the Gadarene swine to make up his outfit. And, if I ever penetrated into his private room it would be to see him standing, with his coat and waistcoat off and the immensely long line of his perfectly elegant trousers from waist to boot heel. And he would have a slightly reflective air and he would be just opening one kind of case and just closing another.' Next line, start of new paragraph: 'Good God, what did they all see in him?'

Ford Madox Ford's John Dowell, Conrad's Charles Marlow, Scott Fitzgerald's Nick Carraway . . . It seems to be a mostly male thing: these plausible, unreliable narrators.

Another thing I don't know is which books were on a mid-20th-century white girl's reading list. *Little Women*? I think many girls read boys' books, because they were the ones lying around, but those books came with a Health & Safety warning: if you are a girl, don't try this at home. In patriarchal societies the combination of women and books is perceived as even more threatening than either on their own. In Flaubert's *Madame Bovary*, Emma's dissatisfaction with her marriage is specifically linked to her reading: first, the novels smuggled into her convent school by a seamstress ('They were about love, lovers, loving, martyred maidens swooning in secluded lodges, horses ridden to death on every page, dark forests, aching hearts . . .'); then Walter Scott ('She would have liked to live in some old manor house, like those chatelaines in their long corsages . . . looking out far across the fields for the white-plumed rider galloping towards her on his black horse'); later, the new novels delivered from Paris: 'she read Balzac and George Sand, seeking to gratify her secret cravings'. Flaubert's novel spelled out the evidence for its own prosecution. The trial of *Madame Bovary* for obscenity in 1857 was an attempt not to ban its publication – photo studios and shops selling pornography were flourishing in Paris at the time – but to prevent women from reading.

In October 1960, a century after the prosecution of *Madame Bovary* in France and while I aged nine was sitting in a leather armchair in my all-boys school library, Mr Mervyn Griffith-Jones, chief counsel for the prosecution in the trial of *Lady Chatterley's Lover* for obscenity, suggested to the jury in Number 1 Court at the Old Bailey that they should ask themselves: 'Is it a book you would wish your wife or your servant to read?' The jury comprised nine men and three women. Again: You, sir, may be trusted with this book, but heaven forfend that it should be read by women and the working classes.

Robyn heard out my explanation of Jack Robinson and then told me about another book she doesn't think is written by the author named on the title page. She has just started a new novel by a writer she admires and this is a tense moment. Turn down the music, put the monkey in its cage. And for Robyn, this new one doesn't ring true. The writer has been hacked into. It's like when someone starts speaking and their voice doesn't go with their face, their whole body. On the other hand, Robyn says, there's a short novel by a Brazilian writer that was published a decade ago, translated from the Portuguese, that she thinks *is* by the writer she admires. The writer was trying something different, she had written herself into a corner and was trying to break out, so she took a pen name to bypass the expectations her previous work had set up. To Robyn it feels completely authentic. Is that the right word? If she did some research she thinks she could prove it but her job is low pay, long hours, and she doesn't have the time. She says I can borrow the book if I want, and because I think she is setting me a kind of test I accept it. But she does want the book back: it's out of print, she found it in a second-hand bookshop.

In second-hand bookshops, certain books are almost guaranteed. Did everyone give copies of these books to everyone else, and no one really wanted them? Did anyone actually read them? A bonus in these shops is the ephemera used as bookmarks by previous owners: bus tickets, shopping lists, postcards and envelopes, some with route directions and phone numbers. Often there are records of a previous reader's engagement in the form of underlined sentences and comments in the margins: 'Yes!!!', 'very moving', 'cf Yeats Byzantium', 'Dear Jean-Paul – How can you be sometimes so smart and sometimes so stupid?' The last comment was written by David Markson in the margin of a book by Sartre. After Markson's death in 2010 the contents of his personal library were found scattered among the stacks and pavement carts of the Strand bookstore in New York. There was online discussion: some considered this random dispersal a fitting legacy, others argued that the collection should have been kept intact in a university archive. Academics sighed, fans and pigeons flocked, ships of state went sailing by.

A local second-hand bookshop has shelves labelled 'Cult': Burroughs, Bukowski, Anaïs Nin and the Marquis de Sade and books on witchcraft, Charles Manson and Jack the Ripper. We seekers after holy relics on dusty shelves are ourselves a cult, poking about among the ruins. In David

Hare's film *Wetherby*, Marcia, a librarian, is driving with a friend to a jumble sale with boxes of second-hand clothes. The man expounds a theory – he's read it in a book – that 'murder is characteristically committed by people who handle other people's things. In second-hand clothes shops, junk shops, markets . . . Self-improvement, that's another hallmark. People who teach themselves things, at home, at night . . . A fantasy life of singular intensity.' Marcia suggests that the man is keen on murder himself: 'Yes, oh God, yes, I'm addicted.' In turn, he asks, 'Do *you* like murder?' and Marcia replies: 'Not much. But I prefer it to romance.'

Sir Thomas Phillipps, 1792–1872, spent his family wealth on collecting books: he wanted to own a copy of every book in the world. A flag flaps in the breeze above a coastal fort; loaded with booty from the hinterland, a line of wagons trundles across a plain, overseen by a red-faced man with gonorrhoea and a whip.

'Go, litel book.' Go where? Most books end up with Bohumil Hrabal's Mr Haňt'a – who, standing in the sunshine with a few beers inside him on the street outside his workplace, where he operates a press for compacting trash, sees 'an enormous bale standing on a deserted plain, a cube fifteen hundred feet long, maybe longer, with all Prague compacted in it, myself included, all my thoughts, all the books I'd ever read, all my life, and it was all nothing more than the tiniest of mice being crushed with the wastepaper in my cellar by the Brigade of Socialist Labor'. Hrabal's *Too Loud a Solitude*

is an elegy for a lost Golden Age of rubbish, when most of
it was biodegradable and its scale was manageable – Haňt'a
is eventually put out of his job by a new compactor whose
operatives wear 'orange and baby-blue gloves and yellow
American baseball hats' – and prominent in the welter of
rubbish dumped upon Haňt'a are books: fittingly, he feels,
'living as I do in a land that has known how to read and write
for fifteen generations; living in a onetime kingdom where it
was and still is a custom, an obsession, to compact thoughts
and images patiently in the heads of the population, thereby
bringing them ineffable joy and even greater woe'. Some of
the books he takes home: they are shelved on planks 'above
the toilet bowl, about five feet off the floor' and also above
his bed, so that 'when I fall asleep I've got all those books
weighing down on me like a two-ton nightmare'. Many others
– Goethe, Schiller, Nietzsche, Hölderlin, Kant – go straight
into the compacted bales, though sometimes Haňt'a turns
a few pages and lets a sentence or two lodge in his brain.
Haňt'a: 'I am nothing but a refined butcher. Books have
taught me the joy of devastation . . .' Haňt'a's uncle also likes
rubbish: he collects bits of scrap metal, places them on the
tracks on which he runs a restored locomotive, and names
them 'according to the wild shapes they had assumed'. Then
the uncle himself becomes rubbish: in the signal tower he
has built in his garden he has a stroke, and by the time he is
found he is 'coated with flies and worms, his body running
over the linoleum like an overripe Camembert'. Haňt'a
scrapes up 'the remains of his remains' and trowels them
into a coffin, adding boxes of scrap metal and a volume of
Immanuel Kant before the lid is nailed on.

I'm assuming that Robyn has an agenda. I'm assuming that sooner rather than later she is going to slide some of her own writing across the table in a plain brown envelope or send it as an email attachment with a half-joking, half-earnest cover note, and it's going to get tricky. You can tell someone you think their partner is an idiot and their dog is ugly and carry on drinking, said Ian Hamilton, but if you tell them you don't rate their *writing* that's the end of a friendship. Or Robyn is going to ask my advice about creative writing courses or finding an agent and I'll tell her I don't have a clue, and she's going to interpret this as me backing away and not taking her seriously. I'll tell her I am not an 'expert' and she'll think this is false modesty. This will happen. And then I think, Robyn is probably wondering what *my* agenda is, in agreeing to meet and talk to her. I wonder too.

Living in Winchelsea in East Sussex in his late twenties, at the start of the 20th century, Ford Madox Ford established 'a very considerable degree of intimacy' with Henry James, who lived in Rye, just two miles away, and was thirty years older. They had separate circles of friends but 'in the winters, when London visitors were scarce, he would come to tea every other day with almost exact regularity, and I would walk back with him to Rye. On the alternate days I would have tea with him and he would walk back to Winchelsea, in all weathers, across the wind-swept marshes.' What did they talk about, as their coat-tails flapped in the wind? Other writers (James 'expressed intense dislike for Flaubert, who "opened his own door in his dressing-gown"'); America ('"Don't talk such damnable nonsense!" He really shouted those words with a male fury');

21

James's financial investments and 'domestic arrangements' . . . Ford never really knew 'what it *was*', this relationship with the Master. He reckoned that for James he was simply 'le jeune homme modeste': respectful, interested, harmless. There are men who have chosen their wives on this basis. It had nothing to do with Ford's own writing: 'Once, after I had sent him one of my volumes of poems, he just mentioned the name of the book, raised both his hands over his head, let them slowly down again, made an extraordinary, quick grimace, and shook with an immense internal joke . . .'

'Be sure that a life of humiliation and disappointment is what you really want': Dai Vaughan's reply to an interviewer asking if he had any 'tips for aspiring writers'. Did he say that with a straight face or a scrunched grin? He was never going to suggest hiring a tax adviser with specialist knowledge of offshore accounts, but is it as bad as that? It depends on what writers are aspiring *to*.

Coleridge's advice to aspiring writers, in *Biographia Literaria*: 'With no other privilege than that of sympathy and sincere good wishes, I would address an affectionate exhortation to the youthful literati, grounded on my own experience. It will be but short; for the beginning, middle, and end converge to one charge: *never pursue literature as a trade*.' His italics, not mine. He meant *get a proper job* and do your writing in the off-hours, 'unannoyed by any alien anxiety'. Would Coleridge have considered teaching creative writing a proper job or just a variant form of being 'a mere literary man'? It does at least get you out of the house, which for Coleridge – who assumes that those 'who in early life feel themselves disposed to become authors' are exclusively male – is another advantage of proper jobs: they 'add a superior chance of happiness in domestic life, were it only that it is as natural for the man to be out of the circle of his household during the day, as it is meritorious for the woman to remain for the most part within it'. Some writers may be better at their other jobs than they are at writing: emotional investment and a need for approval can get in the way.

'Aspiring' writers are hungry for all the help they can get, and 'established' writers are often generous with their tips, but the whole business of tipping is messy. Robyn knows this; she's a waitress. 'How-to-write' books make me uneasy, not least because, like advertising, they contain so many sentences in the imperative mood: do this, don't do that. Best help is caught on the wing. But here's an interesting imperative from Annie Dillard's *The Writing Life*: 'One of the few things I know about writing is this: spend it all, shoot it, play it, lose it, all, right away, every time.' She means, as she then spells out, if while writing a thought or image arrives unbidden, use it, don't keep it 'for a later place in the book, or for another book'. And within a couple of sentences this writerly advice has mutated into something larger: 'Similarly, the impulse to keep to yourself what you have learned is not only shameful, it is destructive. Anything you do not give freely and abundantly becomes lost to you. You open your safe and find ashes.' Good writing as good living: who knew?

Writing is work but unless you're a salaried journalist it is not a 'job'. You cannot both write seriously and expect to be rewarded for this by a system you are intelligent enough to oppose. I want to get that said and out of the way. Also worth getting out of the way: at no stage will Robyn and I be sharing a bed, it's not that kind of book.

Robyn asks: How did Jennie get onto a title page? So again I explain. I was writing a short novel and it was going sluggishly and then early one morning a female character stepped forward and demanded first-person narration and suddenly the writing woke up, and because this was one of the first four CBe books I needed a pen name. Would it be too much to say that I felt released by the voice I had taken over, or that had taken over me? In the circumstances – embedded in my customary, diligent voice – no, it would not be too much. Writing as a woman was liberating, in a way that acts of transgression can be (no guarantee), and I'd be happy to talk more about this but Robyn says no, she meant *How did I get away with it?* This was a decade ago, longer, I tell her. She looks at me as if I've just told her the dog ate my homework, an excuse so shamelessly taking the piss that if I can't come up with anything better, and fast, she is going to immediately give me an after-school detention. I tell her there are precedents, among them a novel titled *Amazons* and subtitled *An Intimate Memoir by the First Woman to Play in the National Hockey League* which Don DeLillo published in 1980 under a female pen name, Cleo Birdwell: 'my honey blond hair flying in the breeze, my silver skate blades flashing, my plucky work in the corners, my style, my stamina, my milky blue eyes,

my taut ass and firm breasts, the nightmarish bruises on my
downy white thighs . . .' Robyn doubles my detention.

Children like to hide – under tables, in dens in the wood –
and there are more of us than you might think, us writers
slipping by under names that are not our own. There are
wives and husbands who don't know that their partners are
published authors. (No one chooses their sexual partners
on the basis of what they *write*. If they do, they're in for a
surprise.) The motivation may be commercial: an agent has
written (in the magazine of the Society of Authors) that when
working with an author whose sales have been dipping, she
may suggest that the author take another name and sell their
new work as a debut novel. Or an author may choose to
keep their desk tidy by publishing their fiction, non-fiction,
poetry and erotica under different names. Or authorship may
conflict with the writer's other interests: Edgar Lee Masters
published, notes Alejandro Zambra, 'under a pseudonym,
as was appropriate for a lawyer who wanted to remain
respectable'. Or an author's real name may already belong to
another author, or to a game-show host or a lousy politician.
Or an author might think that if simply being a writer is
enough to make people suspicious, they have nothing to
lose by adding another reason. Or an author (often a more
complicated animal than is strictly necessary) cannot quite
believe that they have written a book and it makes more sense
to them for it to have been written by someone else – third-
person narration rather than first-person may be their whole
mode of living. (I've tried to practise this when dealing with
physical pain: it's not me that's hurting, it's someone else.

But *who*? And one fine or rainy day will that someone turn up to exact revenge for the pain I've offloaded onto them?) Or at base there may simply be a child who likes secrets and codes and dressing up. Mischief is the only way that children have of getting even with the adult world, and they'll push it as far they can get. Coming out to Robyn (Jack = me, Jennie = me) has been a relief. When in a *TLS* review of a book by Jack Robinson (a review whose rank refusal to engage with the book still makes me angry) the writer ignored the name on the title page and used my real name – 'It's pleasant to meet Mr Boyle here: he's a well-read, well-meaning and genial writer, and a helpful introducer of shy books. But his target is missed by a country mile': the smile and then the knife – I knew the game was up. In fact the game had been up for some time: I had long since lost track of who knew I was Jack and who didn't; and when the writing of a certain other author was attributed to me, my denial only added to the speculation. I was bad at brand management.

Harry Mathews, American writer in Paris in the early 1970s, was suspected of working for the CIA, and the more he denied it the more it stuck. In Mathews' 'autobiographical novel' *My Life in CIA* a woman friend advises him to 'make the role your very own': as a writer he knows how to make up things that people want to hear, and besides, 'think of all the women who are dying to get into bed with a real spy!' Mathews sets up a travel agency as a front and gets into a whole mess. I wouldn't recommend this. Years later, in the 1990s, he overhears a man in a restaurant in Berlin tell his companion that Mathews 'did oddball things that made it risky for everybody involved' and was 'terminated with extreme prejudice'.

I live down the road from a man who chooses to call himself the Earl of Kensington. I once asked him why he was limping and he replied that there was nothing wrong with his leg, he was just 'getting into character'. As well as being an undertaker he has played small-time villains in TV crime series, and has been arrested on suspicion of murder and then released. Another local man used to knock on my door and ask for a tenner: 'Just to see me through the weekend, you'll get it back on Monday, promise.' Mondays came and went. He has always called me Raymond. Inevitably he, for me, is Raymond, the name he's decided is mine and which I've slapped back on him in revenge. The true Raymond eludes us both.

'Just sign here, please.' Any squiggle will do. I'm being asked to witness the delivery of a parcel, or to promise that if I slip in the shower and break my ankle no one will get sued. It's not exactly an *autograph* of the kind that used to be collected in albums, along with stamps and cigarette cards.

What's in a name, anyway? In the case of Brecht, several other names – Elisabeth Hauptmann, Margarete Steffin, Ruth Berlau, Helene Weigel – which didn't even make it to the acknowledgements pages, let alone the title pages. Books are not produced solo, in isolation, but in collaboration with friends, colleagues, partners, lovers, other writers, the dead as well as the living; with those who have taught, or teased, or confided, or nudged open a little door, or whispered sweet nothings that turn out to be far from nothings and often not sweet, or made moves on the dance floor that the writer hadn't even known were possible. It's an ugly word, 'collaboration': I'm seeing those photos taken after the liberation of Paris in 1944 of women having their heads shaved because they had slept with the enemy. A glance from Robyn: no need to spell it out, more than half the population are on a hiding to nothing. 'Acknowledgements' isn't a much prettier word: with too many syllables for the simple act of saying thank you, it suggests a quasi-legal obligation to name the whole gang – agents, editors, researchers. But surely those people are just doing their jobs, and getting paid for it? Why them rather than the café down the road with good soup and the bin men who collect the rubbish first drafts? There's such a thing as common courtesy, Robyn says.

Film credits do list the cafés and the bin men, and the gaffers and best boys and wardrobe assistants. At the end of a film I stay in my seat, bunching up my knees to let others squeeze by while I read the names scrolling by, so fast and so many that they drift into anonymity, as on war memorials, with just the occasional jolt of recognition: 'Additional dialogue by William Shakespeare' (in the credits for *My Own Private Idaho*).

I sent drafts of this book to three honest people who read and responded but they're unlikely to read the book again, now it's in print, because they've read it already and there are so many other books to read, so they're going to miss out on how it's changed *because* they read it, all the deletions and additions, including this one. But thank you.

Dream. I'm in an underground car park, which we know from films is not a place where good things happen, and it's dark and damp and cold and I'm walking towards my car – I don't have a car but in the dream I do, and it's black – when I become aware that between me and my car a figure is standing. Robyn. I can't see her face but I know it's Robyn because she's holding her yellow cycling helmet in her left hand and in her right hand she is holding by its narrow end something about the size and shape of a leg of lamb.

I mention that I recently read in a novel, and not for the first time, that a girl over a certain age always knows when she is being looked at by a man who finds her attractive, even if she doesn't know the source of the gaze, and Robyn asks me if I believe everything I read in books. Of course not. Together we watch a woman coming out of the tube station, walking out of shadow and into sunlight, and suddenly without breaking stride she yawns, she is tired of all this shit.

Glass of wine, glass of water, food. Temperate habits. A friend of a friend did meet that author, the one whose door I didn't

knock on, though 'met' is stretching it a bit and he didn't
know it at the time. He was staying in a hotel in Morocco,
south of Marrakech, and there was this American woman
who sat at a table by herself in the dining room. You would
think they'd have spoken, two foreigners thrown together in a
country where they didn't speak the language, but they didn't.
They nodded in the lobby, passing by. It wasn't an expensive
hotel. The friend of a friend lost his key and the man at the
reception desk opened a drawer and told him to pick another
– any key in that hotel opened any door. When he went out
into the streets he was always surrounded by beggars but
they never approached *her*, even though the assumption is
that women are more likely to give. Years later the friend of
a friend read in a biography that she had spent some time in
Morocco and he did the maths and he reckons it was her. She
went on record as saying that biography was a pack of lies, but
still. She smoked cigarillos. She was left-handed.

John Berger on Giorgio Morandi: 'That he was left-handed
is, I feel, important but I do not know why.' I paused. I still
like that sentence, and I do not know why, except that I
happen to be left-handed myself. I also happen to physically
resemble – or I used to physically resemble – the American
actor Billy Bob Thornton, and have wondered if *he* is left-
handed. In the photographs he holds a cigarette (or a Golden
Globe) sometimes in his right hand, sometimes in his left.
The film in which our resemblance is closest is the Coen
Brothers' *The Man Who Wasn't There*, in which Billy Bob
plays a barber's assistant ('Sooner or later everyone needs a
haircut') and chain-smokes through the entire action. The last

time I watched the film I kept count: the cigarette is in Billy Bob's right hand more often than in his left. He might be ambidextrous. The clincher is when he kills a man: the knife is in his right hand, so I probably have to accept that he is right-handed.

At the café where Robyn works there's a new regular, a man who sits by the window with his laptop and stretches a double espresso over as long as two hours while he writes. He is friendly and they have talked, Robyn and this man. He has pitched an essay about living in London as a freelance writer to one of the magazines, and they've accepted it. People are interested in money – how can anyone without a regular income even afford to *breathe* in this run-for-maximum-profit city? – and the social-media feedback will be good for the circulation figures. The man is in his twenties, Robyn tells me, and his first novel will be coming out in the spring. Not many people can afford to sit around in cafés in central London writing essays about writing.

I don't back up my work regularly because that would be to admit that my laptop isn't as reliable as they tell me it is and as I want to believe it is. In other words, Robyn tells me, I don't back up regularly because I'm stupid.

Reader, I married him – Robyn getting a little carried away. She once wrote to a certain author, care of her publishers. A kind of thank-you letter, she says, very polite. Two or three letters, she adds, when I ask if that was the only one. Not more than half a dozen. She never got a reply. She wasn't expecting one, she says. To be fair, she probably didn't want to *marry* that author, she just wanted to see what was on their shelves while they were making tea, and look at the view out of the window above the writing desk. This was when she was young – but she is *still* young. I was born in a library and have mostly lived there ever since; Robyn was born in a smartphone.

Paris, Easter 1973. At the Coupole – which has a last-century literary heritage and along with photographs of Hemingway incorporates many naked women in its décor – the Australian novelist Murray Bail watches a white-haired old man trying to sharpen a ballpoint pen with a razor blade.

Robyn points out that many of the books on my reading list from 1963 – all those Buchans and Rider Haggards – featured the all-action male hero: the man who leaps across chasms (*yawning* ones) and triumphs single-handedly over the evil forces that threaten to destroy civilisation. Where has he gone to? Into the Bond films is one place, but I don't want to follow him there because that place is a trap. Do I miss him? He was around long before 1963, I say: he used to kill dragons. And rescue damsels in distress, Robyn adds. It was part of the job description. Robyn tells me there's a new male character who has been appearing in recent fiction so often that he too is becoming a type. He is witty and widely read but he doesn't interview well. He can't afford membership of a fitness gym and even if he could he'd spend the money on booze instead,

because fitness gyms are part of the sleek corporate world
he despises on principle, a principle that means when he
needs to upgrade his iPhone he also has to despise himself.
Relationships with women: it's complicated. He is feckless, in
a way that's designed to come across as harmless. Robyn isn't
so sure.

'Inspiring,' says Robyn. 'Turgid piffle,' I say. She thinks I
am being cynical and ungenerous. I try to explain to Robyn
the concept of, in Nabokov's preferred transliteration of
this Russian term in his book on Gogol, *poshlust*. This isn't
easy. 'The dreadful thing about *poshlust*,' writes Nabokov,
'is that one finds it so difficult to explain to people why a
particular book which seems chock-full of noble emotion and
compassion is far, far worse than the kind of literature which
everybody admits is cheap.' *Poshlust* can sometimes be 'the
obviously trashy' but is 'also the falsely important, the falsely
beautiful, the falsely clever, the falsely attractive'. *Poshlust* is
often 'so cleverly painted all over with protective tints that its
presence (in a book, in a soul, in an institution, in a thousand
other places) often escapes detection'. An author's being
'perfectly honest and sincere (as the saying goes)', Nabokov
goes on in his seigneurial way, 'cannot prevent the demon
of *poshlust* from possessing himself of an author's typewriter
when the man lacks genius and when the "reading public" is
what publishers think it is'. *Poshlust* spreads like an infestation.
Nabokov quotes reviews from an ad for a book in a newspaper
on his desk – 'The work of a master psychologist who can
skillfully probe the very inner recesses of men's souls', etc. –
and notes that 'the "beautiful" novel is "beautifully" reviewed

and the circle of *poshlust* is complete'. Robyn nods. She's got it. We each propose examples of acclaimed novels and discuss whether they are infected by 'the furtive and clammy touch of *poshlust*'. Robyn suggests that women writers may be less prone to *poshlust* just because, historically, they have done less banging on about the noble and heroic virtues of mankind, those virtues being to them less self-evident.

Outside the café in Lisbon he used to frequent there's a statue of Pessoa sitting at a bronze table, with a second bronze chair 'so you can be photographed sitting next to him by someone', as Frederick Seidel puts it in his poem 'Lisbon'. I sit down at the table with Pessoa. In the pseudonymity business, he's the boss, but I don't think we're going to hit it off: 'Talking to others makes me shudder. If they show any interest in me, I flee.' That's from *The Book of Disquiet*, which I first attempted to read twenty years ago. I didn't get far: too much lassitude and prim distaste for other people ('In modern life the world belongs to the stupid, the insensitive and the disturbed'). But no one can finish this book, anyway: it doesn't have a beginning or end and even its middle is unstable. There are at least three different editions in English translation, of varying lengths, in print. The book isn't even by Pessoa: most of it is by one of his heteronyms, Bernardo Soares, though Pessoa did admit that of his four principal others Soares was closest to the person he believed himself to be, being 'a simple mutilation of my own personality'. *The Book of Disquiet* is saturated with the absence of that mutilated 'personality'. Soares/Pessoa writes continually of his *not being there*: 'I look for myself but find no one'; 'I write like someone asleep'; 'I know that I was never anything but error and mistake'; 'Only disguised am I myself.' A whorled shell is being exquisitely constructed from within.

For Soares/Pessoa, love is not on the menu: 'Only someone lacking all aesthetic sense could possibly love me and if they did, I would despise them for it.' He's simply not that interested in other people. Very occasionally, something slips through. He mentions that in his early childhood his father killed himself while living far away (as for why his father was absent, 'I never particularly wanted to know'). When the news of his father's death arrived, people looked at him at mealtimes and he looked back, 'in clumsy incomprehension'; then he went back to his food, but eating very carefully in case the others were still looking at him.

I ask Robyn how she's getting along with the book I lent her in return for the maybe-not-Brazilian one and she says, *Which book?* A first edition of a novel published in the 1950s by a writer now forgotten but who deserves to be brought back into print. I don't want to fetishise every out-of-print book I'm fond of, and I didn't talk about this book with Robyn before I lent it to her – I wanted her to read it without me looking over her shoulder – but my lending the book was a signal that I trusted her. She didn't have to acknowledge that signal. She didn't even have to read the book. But I lent it to her, and I very rarely lend books, and now Robyn is not only telling me that this transaction never happened but *shrugging.*

I returned to *The Book of Disquiet*. The mistake I'd made earlier was to slip into the habit of identifying with the 'I' character. Anything so crass is fended off: 'I never wanted to be understood by other people. To be understood is akin to prostituting oneself.' In adolescence, that no-one-understands-me schtick (and they couldn't possibly understand me anyway, because I am so uniquely sensitive) just about works, but I'm now at a biblical age. Soares/Pessoa defines 'the central error of the literary imagination' as 'the idea that other people are like us and must therefore feel like us'. For the second reading, I stayed outside the window of Soares' room on the Rua dos Douradores, or on my side of the table in the Café A Brasileira, watching him at work: 'For me, to write is to despise myself, but I can't stop writing.' He far prefers writing to living, 'even if living means no more than buying bananas in the sunshine': he worries that 'They might not wrap the bananas properly' and that 'My voice might sound odd when I ask the price.' He admits that he once wanted to be a travelling salesman, but 'perhaps my greatest aspiration really does not go beyond occupying this chair at this table in this café'. A salesman of what, I wonder: encyclopaedias? Cosmetics? Lingerie? On Christmas Day in 1929 Pessoa paces his room in his slippers and 'posthumous coat' and identifies with 'one of those damp cloths used to clean grimy objects in the house that get taken to the window to dry but instead are left there, screwed up on the sill that they slowly stain'. Pessoa at his café table is a sit-down comedy act; it won't top the ratings but it's long-running and has had great reviews.

Do writers who claim not to read the reviews of their books really not read them? Not even a sly look online after everyone else has gone to bed? They don't read them, I assume, because they worry the reviews would make them depressed or – far worse – that they would acquire an intolerable sense of self-esteem. Most books are lucky to get *any* review. Newspapers are *news*papers and will review a new book by a well-known author because that is news, and a book *about* a well-known author and a book by a retired (and not before time) prime minister and a book that has caused a Twitter storm because those too are news, as news is reckoned, but this and 99 per cent of other books are not news.

Death can help. Dying can lever an author off the review pages and onto the news pages and be good for sales. This must be annoying: they would have preferred the new sales income while they were still around to spend it. Now, having exited, they are suddenly called back on stage while the audience discusses their position in the rankings. To step back from all that is a way of saying 'Time will tell', but time often says nothing all. That verdict can be appealed but it's a lengthy process.

I like reading reviews of books which, because of the fickle god who decides which books get translated into English and which not, I may never read. It's a way of listening in to the conversation, even if I don't always follow what's being said. The authors of these books are like characters written by the writers who tell me about them. I nod to them as I might to a neighbour from down the road who is familiar, even though we have never spoken.

The people sitting at other tables in the cafés where Robyn and I meet, who do they think we are? Not jobbing writer and ardent reader. We don't have our laptops with us so we can't be work colleagues discussing sales figures on spreadsheets. Lovers? We are not giving off any of the signs. Uncle and niece, meeting to discuss the niece's student loan? Different generations, certainly. Many of my habits and literary tastes were developed when you could smoke on the top deck of buses. We are both certifiably middle class. And we both know that this is just a phase in our lives, that the only thing that brings us together is this book and that unless something weird happens it is very unlikely our paths will cross again after page 175. The same happens with most lovers and work colleagues.

A woman who is probably Robyn's age but looks older suddenly leans across and I think she is about to ask for money for a hostel bed but no, it's more complicated: her dad has had a stroke and is in hospital she needs to get to Newcastle and the coach fare is £26.50 and the last coach today leaves just after six . . . Robyn gives her a couple of pounds. I've got nothing smaller than a tenner and I'm not going to give her that. She blows me a mocking kiss and stomps on to the next table. I am a mean bastard. I ask Robyn if she believes the woman's story and she says of course not but it was plausible, wasn't it? She had researched it: coach fare, departure times. Besides, Newcastle is where Robyn's own father happens to live, and he lives alone and smokes too much and she worries about him. So she gives money according to how 'realistic' a story is? Yes, on the whole. That, and other things: how well the story is told; whether it touches a nerve; the mood of the moment. She suspects that those begging in cafés and bars do better in the evenings, after alcohol has loosened the purse strings, but the coach to Newcastle will have left by then.

Robyn's father used to build boats and was made redundant and now he sits at home making scale models of clippers, the 19th-century sailing ships designed to carry tea and opium fast from China. Just clippers, or other ships too? I'd like to see those models. I ask Robyn if she has any photos of them and she looks at me as if I've strayed off the path.

I have given Robyn back the book she lent me, the one she believes is not by the Brazilian author named on the title page, and she wants to know what I think. 'I don't know.' Is that bad? I'm disappointing Robyn here, because the book means a lot to her and expressing opinions is our unwritten contract, but some books just sit there on the shelf, *taking up space*. Maybe it was simply the wrong kind of book for the day on which I read it. As in, 'the wrong kind of snow'. If you were in bed with tonsillitis, you'd probably leave the 'challenging' new experimental novel on the table. About the book Robyn lent me, I can say it's short and the writing (or the translation) is perfectly competent, but I have no idea why

Robyn believes it is not what it claims to be. She is welcome to try to persuade me. I often need things pointing out to me.

Many people not only don't have a strong opinion about Hardy's Wessex novels but don't even know what they really *want*. I mean people in the West, not the people who are coming to the West as refugees; I mean my tribe, the people who already have a 'better life' – and then what? Books are not the answer. They try to be, with absolute sincerity, while knowing they are going to fail. *Almost* is exactly their appeal. *Almost* is also their get-out clause when people turn on them in disappointment.

Very few writers have published just one book: 'There, I've said what I wanted to say, I don't want to say it again and now I'm going fishing.' On the other hand, plenty of writers are known to most readers for a single book despite their having written many others. This can happen when a book is made into a film with famous actors. There are small towns that become widely known for a single newsworthy event, sometimes a by-election upset but more often a massacre of schoolchildren, and it can take a generation or two for drivers not to make that association when they see the town's name on a sign on the motorway.

I have been stood up. Just as I'm sitting down in the place where I've invited Robyn to lunch I get a text saying that she's had to cover for another waiter who has called in sick. Robyn's café is only a few streets away, so I go round. Everything is normal: sunshine, slightly cloudy, flat whites and toasted paninis, sorry no avocado today; but no one has called in sick and Robyn is not there. I feel a flicker of annoyance but I can't indulge that because last week I stood *her* up – there she was, twiddling her thumbs, while I was having a mid-afternoon nap. In the end I decide that Robyn deserves applause for acting so *out of character*.

Still nothing from Robyn. I've called but she's not picking up. She's been knocked off her bike by a truck and is lying in hospital swathed in bandages; she's gone to Paris for a week with the man who is writing the essay on the freelance life in London; her father has had a stroke and she has gone up to Newcastle; she's been kidnapped by aliens and transported to another planet; or, quite simply, she has grown tired of our chats and wants out. What kind of book is this, anyway? Am I one of those authors who have everything planned out before they write the first sentence, or the other kind, who let the characters take over? The latter, but it's awkward. Is Robyn my stooge, puppet, foil? Watson to my Holmes, Jeeves to my Wooster, Wise to my Morecambe, Son to my Steptoe? Girl in sequins posed against a board I throw knives at? Is Robyn myself, half a century younger? Because of the awkwardness, I try to make good by being punctual (and taking care with punctuation).

My father was punctual to a fault. I will tell Robyn about the time my father had to travel to Glasgow and got to the station platform so early he boarded the wrong train and found himself in Sheffield, and as I remember this my father, who has been dead for 65 years, rolls his eyes and says, Please, can't you tell her a different story? I didn't spend all my life in railway stations.

Books also can arrive too early or too late. In the handwritten list of 54 rejections that David Markson compiled as he sent out *Wittgenstein's Mistress* and it kept bouncing back, one publisher is quoted thus: 'Brilliant. 25 years ahead of its time. No.' Was Markson supposed to put the manuscript in his drawer and send again after 25 years? Or find another publisher whose office clock was running a bit faster? In the short term, the most successful books are those which arrive bang on time. In the long term, punctuality probably doesn't matter; many books now continuously in print sold barely a handful when they were first published. While in the badly lit and chilly waiting room, Markson compiled another list, this one of famous writers whose work was serially rejected (Beckett, Golding) or who self-published (Defoe, Thackeray) or whose work was dismissed by other writers (Henry James bored by *Crime and Punishment*, Conrad disliking *Moby-Dick*, Yeats not finishing *Ulysses*). I sense his stubborn pride in compiling this list, in becoming a member of the *salon des refusés*. But he'd have preferred a yes.

Robyn: Portrait of the Artist as a Young Woman? Unformed, callow, testing her limits, falling into the canal and being rescued by a passing stranger. Writing because it feels important (and not asking why). Writing work that will later – after she has 'found her voice' and 'made her name' and after people start saying she is writing 'at the height of her powers' – be described as early and *prefatory* but which just may, because of its awkwardness and honesty, be the best work she ever does.

Women read more books than men. Many men don't read books written by women. A 2018 *New Yorker* piece reported on a survey showing that between 2003 and 2016 the time spent reading by the 'average American reader' went up from 1.39 hours daily to 1.48 hours; but since the number of people doing any reading at all fell from 26.3 per cent of the population to 19.5 per cent during the same period, that's not much comfort. (Is comfort what I want?) I probably spend fractionally more time reading these numbers than I used to, because there's more of them to read and there's safety in numbers. (Safety?) The number of books sold annually in the UK is around 1.9 million, down from around 3.4 million a decade ago. The number of new books published annually in the UK is around 184,000. Is that too many? Too few? Just about right? All of the above?

If you've been brought up not to show off, the *look-at-me!* of your own name on the title page can feel presumptuous. If your social skills are 3/10 and you are lacking in confidence, you may find it easier to inhabit an identity other than your own (shy people can blossom as actors on the stage). If a formative period of your life was lived vicariously through books by other people, this can become a habit that's hard to shift, even if you have to write the books yourself.

The last time we met before she went AWOL, Robyn asked me about the book I mentioned in which she has a part: 'What's it about?' If they knew what their poems were about, poets tend to say, why would they bother writing them? But it's still a fair question. I read Robyn the draft blurb for the back cover, a paragraph that at least gives a clue. But when I say that it's a book about what we talk about when we talk about books, and then list a random number of subjects, some more obviously book-related than others, I mean that it's about the talking as much as about what's being talked about, so about misunderstandings, silences, evasions, forgetfulness, differences that we hope will be reconcilable ones but may not be and sudden unaccountable enthusiasms. Even if much of the time I am talking to myself.

Talk is everyday magic. In a 13th-century Icelandic tale Ivar and his brother are living at the court of the king of Norway. When his brother returns to Iceland, Ivar asks him to tell the woman he loves he'll be back soon and not, please, to marry anyone else in the meantime. The brother marries her himself, and Ivar succumbs to the black dog of depression. The king, who is fond of Ivar, offers him any woman he chooses, or rule over some of the royal estates, or vast wealth. None of these appeals. The king makes a last offer: Ivar is to come to him every day, after the official state business is over, and they will talk together about the woman Ivar loves. They

44

do this, and Ivar's depression lifts. It's a story about books: which cannot reverse or even diminish injustice, but life would be even worse without them. (And I'm interested, in this story, in the woman Ivar loved: she was clearly less patient than he was, and at least in part this may have been why he loved her and still does.)

I'm back at the table in a café where I meet Robyn. A man asks if the chair Robyn usually sits in is free and I want to say, no, I'm sorry, I'm waiting for someone, but he has already thanked me and taken the chair. He is sitting with a group of people who are talking about books, though I could have got this wrong; the number of ambulances passing by with their sirens blaring is bad today. I look at the empty space where Robyn should be sitting and despite or because of the noise of the sirens I can hear myself think that there's a hole in everything I write above which the writing skates nimbly, as in the painting by Raeburn of the Scottish minister which for a reason I forget I always associate with Coleridge; or rather, a blockage, something that prevents the puddles from draining, shivering as the rain pitters down.

I think Robyn had a happy childhood. She's grounded. Though a lot can be disguised and I could be missing the signs. I don't want to say how tall or short she is and what colour hair because although I was once told I have 'a novelist's eye for detail' it's not that kind, but I'll mention that she cycles to her work and brings a clean change of clothes every day in her backpack. There's a question I could ask to which only Robyn will know the answer but I don't know yet what the question is. Quite often I sense that what I'm witnessing is a metaphor for something, without knowing what that something is.

The woman who asked for money for a coach ticket to Newcastle is here again. I ask how her dad is doing but she has a new story today, something about a left-luggage locker, and she blows me a kiss and walks on.

A woman at an outside table is reading a book, so lost to the world that she doesn't even register how her body shifts in her chair to accommodate a stiffness in her elbow. As I cross the street a waitress approaches the reader and they talk and I see that the reader is Robyn, but she's still not yet 'my book friend'. Then she looks up and greets me and we slip back into routine. I ask her what she was chatting to the waitress about and she says shop talk. For people who serve in cafés, do I know who the most irritating customers are? The ones who try to help. It's *her* job to stack the dirty plates and glasses on the table and she can do it better and faster than them. The rude ones, the fussy ones, those you can just ignore.

She's back. She is tired. Not exhausted; she doesn't exaggerate. She's been holed up in her flat reading all of the novels shortlisted for a prize. I'm guessing there were six books, because that's the holy number: one a day for six days and on the seventh day God rested. I ask her which title will win and she tells me which she *thinks* will win and I nod: it speaks to our present sense of crisis, it is required reading for all those in positions of power. Etc. Maybe it *should* win – I don't know,

I haven't read the book, only the reviews. But I am on high alert for the demon of *poshlust*.

What would it take for *me* to behave out of character? I could write a historical romance. Typical, Robyn says. She doesn't mean my writing a historical romance – that might in fact be interesting. She means the way I dodged the question. I change the subject. I sidestep. I take short cuts. I put something in play and I don't follow through. I smoke too much and I laugh too readily at things that are not funny. I am not a serious person. I lack patience. I write some poetry and then stop when it gets difficult. I flirt with fiction. I mock the cosiness of the literary world but I'm not going to bail out because I'm enjoying the comforts it affords me, and without even having had to struggle for those because I had a comp ticket for entry. A meal ticket. And I *know* this – the knowing is part of the package. For me to behave out of character I would have to either jump ship or sign on the dotted line and *join in*, without reservations. Robyn sees me as a character in a play by Chekhov set on a run-down country estate, an unshaved, middle-aged man with talents he never made the most of because he never had to and who drinks too much and keeps looking at the new kitchen maid. No one can remember how he got here, this long-term house-guest with his amusing cynical quips, but he has become part of the furniture. And at the end of the play nothing has changed.

Am I *married* to Robyn?

Robyn continues. If I ask her, she says – I'm not asking,
but she is going to tell me anyway – Geoff Dyer has a lot to
answer for, especially that early book about not writing a
book about D. H. Lawrence, *Out of Sheer Rage*. Dyer rereads
Lawrence's letters and some of the essays but the novels
are hard work, it's easier to riff on some nice places he has
tried to write in. He goes on holiday with his girlfriend to
Lawrence-related shrines around the world and tells us about
his miserable journeys in cars and trains and on ferries and
planes. He writes about his eczema and his alopecia and his
nosebleeds and his problems with his knees, and the time he
spends worrying about not doing the exercises that might help
with his knees, a time much longer than the time it would
take to actually *do* these exercises. He wanks on a beach.
Avoidance, distraction – it's 'a book comprised entirely of
irrelevancies', as Dyer himself says – but because he does all
this with a bundle of wit and charm he not only *gets away with
it* but licenses others to think they can do the same. I agree.
The catch here is that few others have Dyer's wit, let alone his
skill. No, Robyn says. The problem is people believing that
wit and skill are *enough*.

And by the way, Robyn says, she doesn't care for this book's
epigraph. She tells me I'm fond of epigraphs and it's true.
They add a little gravitas. They sit proudly on their dedicated
page, white space galore around them, saying riddle me:
gnomic, unfathomable. Stendhal too was fond of epigraphs
and if he couldn't find anything appropriate he made them
up and attributed them to famous authors. Robyn likes the
epigraph in the Jack Robinson *W12* book, from Pinter's *The*

Caretaker – 'I was never without a piece of soap, whenever I happened to be knocking about the Shepherds Bush area' – but the one from Helen Garner for this book, she says, is too much of a shrug: pretending to be someone other than myself has consequences, and I'm laughing them off.

Dream. At a book launch in a shop where I'm a regular customer the bookseller hands me a letter addressed to me c/o the bookshop. I recognise the handwriting on the envelope. At a corner near the door I place my glass of wine on a shelf and open the letter, which is from Jennie Walker. She looks back on our brief affair with fondness. But life moves on: she fell in love with a woman and went to live with her in Germany. These days she doesn't feel part of the literary world at all, in fact she can't remember the last time she read a book, but if I ever happen to be passing through Heidelberg I am welcome to call by.

On the beach, on the balcony, on the imagined holiday, even in the airport, I read 'The Writer on Holiday' by Roland Barthes, and when I have finished I read it again, because it may be the last word on writers on holiday. A vacation from a vocation? Barthes: 'The singularity of a "vocation" is never better displayed than when it is contradicted – but not denied, far from it – by a prosaic incarnation: this is an old trick of all hagiographies . . . The balance of the operation is that the writer becomes still more charismatic, leaves this earth a little more for a celestial habitat where his pyjamas and his cheeses in no way prevent him from resuming the use of his noble demiurgic speech.' The writer on holiday is 'one of these cunning mystifications which the Establishment practises the better to enslave its writers'.

After reading Robert Lowell on a Greek island Peter Levi wrote a piece in the *TLS* suggesting that a test of a good book was whether it could be enjoyed anywhere, and I have no idea why decades later I still remember that piece because I don't think it's true. Bad books can be enjoyed anywhere too.

For the first time, Robyn asks me for a cigarette. We are smoking the pipe of peace. She apologises for her little rant the other day. She was tired, she has been sleeping badly. I tell her not to apologise: I need her to make me aware of my prejudices. Robyn stubs out her cigarette, grimacing. It's over a year since she gave up smoking. She doesn't take kindly to being assigned the role of teacher's pet, the one who asks intelligent questions. We change the subject. We talk about the ugliness of contemporary car design: so many of them look like bodybuilders, the muscles bulked up and the windows too small. We talk about cricket.

Yorkshire are not having a good season. But the appeal of sport is that at the start of any match – which will be played out according to rules that everyone involved will bend as far as they can – I don't know how it's going to end. It's like reading a new book: it could be a triumph or a disaster or a nil-nil draw in the rain. Some clever people can talk about both books and sport at the same time. My tutor at university recalled going to Twickenham with T. S. Eliot, and Eliot using a passage in play among the backs to illustrate a particular metrical pattern in poetry. Nabokov ('I am good at games, especially at tennis') does the same to illustrate a technique in the writing of Gogol, also at Twickenham: 'Several years ago during a rugby game in England I saw the wonderful Obolensky kick the ball on the run and then changing his mind, plunge forward and catch it back with his hands . . . something of this kind of feat is performed by Nikolai Vassilievich.'

Many literary folk think sport is infantile. How can an intelligent adult be interested in bats and balls? Except in an ironic way, and that would be tedious. All those statistics, those mind-numbing *numbers* (but I suspect many writers check their wordcounts hourly). Class is involved, inevitably: cricket, which has a literary sheen, is permissible, but not darts. (A lesser-known fan of cricket was Mavis Gallant: if it hadn't been for the writing 'I'd be a champion cricket player. Maybe I am a champion cricket player, in another life.') In turn, many sports fans don't get the point of literature. That some writers are as doubtful about literature as sports fans hardly helps its cause. Paul Léautaud, a writer and anthologist (he also cared for several hundred stray cats and dogs, plus a goose and a monkey), wondered how anyone sensible and aged over fifty read could read novels, let alone write them. Romantic novels were the worst: they never told about 'the small, wet mess that follows the embrace'.

Today, Robyn seems *thinner*. Her hair is unwashed, her sleeves are frayed. And she is afraid to go home. Last night, when she tried to sleep she saw this: all the books that she owns trembling on their shelves and then toppling down, slowly at first but quickening to an avalanche. Individual titles were briefly visible, books she'd forgotten she owned, books she thought she'd lost or given away, books she now regrets ever having given shelf space to, books she had never read but one day might get around to, books swallowed up in waves of tumbling others. She woke up in a sweat. She drank a glass of water and then another and tried to read the book on the floor by her bed but the words swam out of focus. Each time she closed her eyes the avalanche was continuing. Sometime around dawn she managed an hour or two of sleep, lying on a blanket on the floor of her tiny kitchen. She was so tired at work this morning she spilled an Americano over a customer. I tell Robyn she can sleep at my place but we both know this wouldn't work: my place too is stacked with books and today any books on shelves, even if they are not *her* books, make her feel queasy. She phones a friend she used to know at college, a friend who is into scuba-diving and who boasts that he got a degree without having read a single book.

The shelves were not the problem. The shelves were sturdy. Robyn had made them herself. One of the several things that Geoff Dyer failed to do while not quite failing to write his book on D. H. Lawrence was assemble a set of flatpack kitchen cupboards, and as soon as she read the word *Ikea* Robyn knew where this was going. For many writers, cack-handedness and innumeracy are badges of honour. Calvino

admits at the start of his essay on rubbish that taking out
the bins is the only household chore in which he can claim
any competence, and that generally in the house he 'is
always getting in the way of everybody else's work'. He can't
even do the shopping; at best he can do 'emergency stopgap
expeditions', and even for these he needs a list of things
to ask for and how much he should be paying. If the toilet
isn't flushing writers get someone in and carry on reading
Baudelaire. I mention to Robyn that the man who fixed my
own toilet was an immigrant from Romania with a PhD in
philosophy and I don't need to rehearse her response: the UK
education system has for centuries reinforced a class-based
master–servant social structure that has rewarded those
who know their Latin from their Greek and taught those
with practical skills to know their lesser place. The fact that
Lawrence himself was an exception to the general ineptitude
of writers – Lawrence could build a whole kitchen from
scratch – was not unrelated to his working-class background.

Cooking, Robyn concedes, is often an exception to the rule
of writers' practical incompetence. Cooking is literary in a
way that plumbing is not. Food offers sensual and aesthetic
pleasures, and men get bonus points for messing around in
the kitchen. (Not Calvino, who can barely deal with an egg:
'there's no way that's a real omelette, it's a forger's hoax, a
charlatan's trick'.) But when people say, about male writers,
he's a good cook, they're usually talking about dinner parties,
they don't mean feeding a family day by day on a tiny budget,
which is what most cooking is.

Thinking that she might as well get paid for some of the reading she does, Robyn has invested in a proofreading course. I could teach her myself but she needs a certificate, she says. She will frame it and hang it on the wall, like the hygiene certificates in cafés. But the course is expensive and today she is not happy. Her bike has been stolen. And that customer she spilt a coffee over – the dry-cleaning bill has been deducted from her wages. I could lend her the money to pay for her course but no, or not yet. Money comes with strings, and they get in a tangle and have to be unknotted.

Robyn's night at the place of her scuba-diving friend didn't go as planned. The friend has two cats, and Robyn is allergic to cats – she gets a rash on her neck, sometimes down to her chest. So she checked into a nearby cheap hotel. The room was perfect: no books, a smell of disinfectant and air-freshener, a damp patch on the ceiling. Just before she went to sleep she had a worrying thought, and she opened the drawer in the bedside table. Relief: no Gideon Bible. Instead, there was a selection of porn magazines. I think that after a couple of nights in that room, a week at most, Robyn will be able to face her bookshelves again.

As well as bookshelves: knick-knacks, postcards, *objets d'art*, clutter, a nice window. The 'Writers' Rooms' photographed for a *Guardian* series a decade ago were disappointing. The promise, the tease, was that given access to the rooms in which books are written, and the writing of books being one of the most private activities that humans engage in, and these writers being good at it, we were going to learn something quasi-magical and unique to that week's author. We didn't. (I liked Alan Sillitoe telling me that 'Sometimes I might just put in a comma in the morning, and take it out again at night.' And Sillitoe's day was long: in at the desk early and 'often still there at 10.30 p.m.') Were they meant to be reassuringly similar, these rooms? – telling me that writers are like not just one another but you and me too? The raffish 'good taste' was not reassuring. It was scary. The rooms of fishmongers or paediatric nurses would have made for a more interesting series. Given the selection of writers featured, the overall message was: writing is a profession for middle-class white males who can afford to live in houses large enough for at least one room to be dedicated exclusively to writing.

Another thing, while I'm here: with just one exception – the photograph of Adam Phillips's room, which showed just part of his desk and a view over a light-industrial rooftop – the photos were composed around the writer's desk and empty chair. We were seeing what the writers see (or don't, because everything is so familiar) when they come into their rooms, not what the writers see as they write. Or what the estate agent sees, when she comes round to give a valuation after the writer has either written a bestseller or gone bankrupt. Adam Phillips: the room 'disappears when I start to work'. The photos were like those ads for trips on steam railways: when you have bought your ticket and taken your seat, you don't see the vintage engines at all, just the same passing landscape you could be looking at from any train.

Stendhal wrote *The Charterhouse of Parma* (more than 500 pages in the current Penguin Classics edition) in 52 days in November and December 1838. (It was published the following April. While most things have got faster, publishing has got slower.) Except that he didn't write it, he dictated it – 'a improvisé et dicté', says the plaque on the building in rue Caumartin, Paris, where this happened, on the fourth floor. In a letter to Balzac Stendhal explained that there were 'sixty or seventy sessions of dictation', and that 'many passages of narrative were left as I dictated them, without any correction'. The means of production – handwriting, typing, dictating, word-processing – surely affects the style of a book. In an afterword to his translation of Gert Hofmann's last novel, *Lichtenberg and the Little Flower Girl*, Michael Hofmann writes that his father suffered a stroke at the age of 57 that left him unable to read, and that for his last three novels he had to devise a new method of composition: 'Where my mother – indispensable to his whole enterprise, and never sufficiently to be praised – had previously typed up fair copies of his manuscripts, she now read drafts back to him, for him to correct and embellish aloud.' As a result, the whole manner of the late books is different: 'The sentences and paragraphs are shorter, the confrontations more present, the scenes seem to ghost in and out, a bigger role falls to diction, to heckles and interjections, to personality.' In the case of Stendhal, dictation suited his fluid, improvisatory style, but I am still a little confused. One biography (by Robert Alter) tells me that Stendhal began dictating from the first day; another (by Jonathan Keates) tells me that first drafts of each section were handwritten, then finished versions were dictated to a 'copyist'. For no good reason, I imagine Stendhal's copyist was a man. I imagine that he lived in the outer suburbs and travelled in to rue Caumartin every morning on a horse-drawn omnibus. I imagine that on most days he carried an umbrella, which before going up to the fourth floor he left with the concierge, who had been instructed to tell all other callers for M. Beyle that he was out of town, and that he always remembered to take back his umbrella before going home, because umbrellas were not cheap. I imagine that he had a young daughter afflicted by an illness that was baffling the doctors, and that at the end of each session Stendhal inquired about this daughter. I imagine that he wrote fast and had very legible handwriting but that sometimes, distracted by worry about his daughter, he made mistakes. I imagine that his daughter survived her illness and that later in her life she read *The Charterhouse* without having any idea that it was her father who wrote it all down.

Such a strange thing to have done, I imagine, to have written a major book. A classic, if you like: one of those books that everyone knows of even if they haven't read it. The odds against this happening are similar to the odds against there being life on Mars. Do the authors of these books know what they have done? Can a classic be written *by accident*? In the same paragraph in which Stendhal records his embarrassment when being complimented in public on his work, he writes: 'I regard, and have always regarded my works as lottery tickets. I don't expect to be reprinted before 1900. Petrarch used to pin his faith on his Latin poem *Africa* and hardly thought about his sonnets.'

John Gale: 'A friend of mine once read *La Chartreuse de Parme* by Stendhal; it inspired him; he determined to change the direction of his life; in the end he just went out and bought himself a new pair of shoes.'

In Walker Percy's *The Moviegoer* the narrator encounters a man who hopes to change the direction of his life by reading *The Charterhouse of Parma* on a bus, thereby demonstrating in public his extreme sensitivity and trusting the world will respond as he deserves. (When I first came to London the books that solitary men in their twenties read while lounging in the café at the ICA were by Camus or Kafka – but Stendhal, why not?) The narrator is curious: is the reader simply someone 'who has an appetite for the book as he might have an appetite for peaches', or is it more about 'the necessity of sticking himself into the world in a certain fashion, of slumping in an acceptable slump, of reading an acceptable book on an acceptable bus'? The latter, clearly: 'too good to be true, this distillation of all graceful slumps'. The reader of Stendhal looks up at the narrator and his own book (*Arabia Deserta*, since you ask) and 'goes into a spasm of recognition and shyness'. The narrator asks the reader how he's getting on with *The Charterhouse*. '"It's – very good," he says at last and blushes. The poor fellow.' He's just a guy who's seeking 'the chance meeting with a chance friend on a chance bus, a friend he can talk to, unburden himself of some of his terrible longings'. Plus the obvious: 'he hopes to find himself a girl, the rarest of rare pieces, and live the life of Rudolfo on the balcony, sitting around on the floor and experiencing soul-communion. I have my doubts.' The narrator is merciless:

this man will 'scare the wits out of some girl with his great choking silences, want her so desperately that by his own peculiar logic he can't have her'.

He's 'a romantic', this reader of The Charterhouse of Parma on a bus, according to Walker Percy's narrator. His 'own peculiar logic' is a Möbius strip that has him luxuriating both in his desire for the idealised girl and in the exquisite melancholy of failure. If he does 'have' the girl, he will flee 'to the islands where, propped at the rail of his ship in some rancid port, he will ponder his own loneliness'. He's dangerous, to himself and others. His choice of reading is apposite: Stendhal, a boy from the provinces with fancy ambitions, was acutely aware of 'the necessity of sticking himself into the world in a certain fashion', and his leading men are constantly putting on an act – most often, that of appearing 'natural' – to achieve their romantic goals (meaning: to get laid). To Robyn this is all drearily familiar. She asks if I've read Stendhal on a bus myself. Yes, almost certainly. She's interested in my relationship with Stendhal, who I'm clearly in love with and who is safely dead. She thinks the man reading The Charterhouse on a bus to New Orleans has listened to some terrible dating tips. There's a lot of bad advice around, not least in literature.

For your average bookaholic – someone who has spent a lot of time looking from the outside in, someone who is not good at talking about their feelings (and there's nothing especially 'English' about this) – shop talk and small talk offer ways of conveying enthusiasm indirectly. Title of my unwritten autobiography: *A Picnic in the Foothills*.

Titles of books that characters in fiction who fancy themselves as authors never get around to writing include: *A History of the Suburbs* (in *Dom Casmurro* by Machado de Assis); *A Short Wait for the Butcher* (in *An Armful of Warm Girl* by W. M. Spackman); *This Is Piccadilly*, in Richard Yates's story 'Liars in Love': 'Ah, Jesus, I could tell you things that'd make your – well, never mind. Skip it.'

The trouble with shop talk, Robyn says, sipping her iced latté, checking an incoming message on her phone, is that by definition it's conservative. It can mock the status quo but only under licence, because the shop itself is part of the status quo. We can come up with ideas as radical as we want but for as long as we live in a capitalist economy we're just tinkering around the edges.

We are sitting at an outside table so I can smoke, and I've just told Robyn that a month ago I found my handwritten list of the books I read in 1963 tucked inside my ancient copy of Chekhov's *Notebook*. At this page: 'The estate will soon be brought under the hammer; there is poverty all round; and the footmen are still dressed like jesters.' Tripartite sentences are like haiku hiding in the bushes. I put Chekhov on the table and then the waiter arrives with our order and as he puts down our cups the coffee gets splashed on the book –

the table is wobbling. Robyn asks if she can borrow my own notebook, and she tears out a couple of blank pages and folds them and folds them again and places this little wedge under one of the table legs, and now there is no wobble. It's not as if I use my notebook for writing in, Robyn points out. I just *carry it around.*

I think that's unfair. *This* is a notebook. Or a journal. It's neither, Robyn says. Some of what's here may have originated in a notebook but it's been dressed up. Notebooks are for rough drafts and notes-to-self and play, nothing buffed and polished. A real notebook contains at least three and often more of the following: paragraphs with crossings-out and circles and arrows; isolated phrases meaningless without a context; snatches of talk overheard on public transport; telephone numbers and song titles and film titles and recipes and route directions; lists of names; illegible sentences written when drunk or very tired; cigarette burns, rings from wine glasses, crusty stains of one or another fluid; ripped edges where pages have been torn out; squashed flies, dried flowers, stray hairs; writing in different coloured inks; titles for poems or stories that will never be written; curses, riddles, prayers; sketches of imaginary animals; pasted-in photographs from magazines. A real notebook *smells*, and not of lavender. A real notebook often has blank pages at the end because all writers at some point, or at recurring points, have dark nights of the soul and want to change their lives and the cheapest way to do this is to start a new notebook.

Georg Christoph Lichtenberg jotted down his aphorisms and irrelevancies in *Sudelbücher*, translated by R. J. Hollingdale as 'waste books': 'a term employed in the English business house of the time to designate the ledgers in which transactions of all kinds were entered as they occurred before being transferred to the more orderly and neatly written account books'. Any school exercise book from the corner shop will do. The shrink-wrapped Moleskine notebooks on the twirly carousels: pass by.

I have difficulty with names, my own not least (*arle*, *oyle*, a gelatinous soup, no snap to it). Ballard took names from the mastheads of American magazines; Henry James copied names from *The Times* into his notebooks. If Flaubert had named Emma Bovary, oh, Gabrielle, or Lisette, would she have had the same life (and death)? If I had been called Jack, same question. Assigning names is a brutal business. Authors and parents name their offspring – who have no say in the matter – with care and diligence, then send them stumbling out into the world to face the consequences.

When I told Robyn that the name I had originally assigned to her was Jackie, she laughed. A cousin of Jack? We laugh often. The alternative is despair. Much writing about sex elicits laughter, especially when the prose is more about the effort put into it – both the sex and the writing – than anything else. Sex is as resistant to language as birth or death; on the other hand, when I'm in a certain mood and the stars are aligned just so, there are times when *all* writing, from

Story of O to *The Marquise of O* to *The Wonderful O* to an Ikea instruction manual, is about sex.

Spoken, words are shaped as they enter the air by rapid little movements of tongue and lips. Something promising there . . . Being read aloud to is a sensory experience. Lyrics are composed to be sung. But written or printed, words are just flat doodles, and getting sex onto the page is difficult. In *On Being Blue*, William Gass notes also the poverty of the available vocab and the tendency of the words that we do have to just get in the way, and that 'the motives of all concerned are usually corrupt'.

Like the stairs or roofbeams in old houses, words creak. Or they scurry behind the skirting boards at night, unafraid of the cat that lies sleeping on my bed. Or huddle close, barely daring to breathe in case it gives them away, on pages whose edges are already turning yellow. They also trip up and collide and collude and blunder through doors just slightly ajar and rarely say what they mean to say, the darlings, because of all the other words jostling around them and the you reading is not the me writing. They play hide-and-seek with the writer, who has only two choices: persevere, or enter a Trappist monastery. Gass's conclusion in *On Being Blue*, which has been forecast by his essay's glorious opening sentence of 26 printed lines and is delivered in a concluding sentence of 42 lines ('So to the wretched writer I should like to say . . .'), is that the only true way to write blue is to caress 'the body of your work itself', to 'give up the blue things of this world in favour of the words that say them'. This is exhilarating. It's also disappointing, because I want to both have my cake and eat it, both the things and the words. Do I really have to give up one 'in favour of' the other? And frustrating, in that the reader (me) is wowed by the choreography of the words at least as much as by what they are telling me.

Edouard Levé: 'I like the flat style of police reports.' There's not much caressing in those. Stendhal, in a letter to Balzac, 1840: 'I know of only one rule: to be *clear* . . . in order to acquire the correct tone I read every morning two or three pages of the Civil Code.' What's being sold here is the 'plain style', often associated with George Orwell: short words rather than long, active rather than passive, no jargon or fancy figurative embellishment, cut and cut again. It has a perceived moral value. It's a style as much as any other and it's damned hard work. Stendhal's letter to Balzac survives in three different drafts.

The difference between Stendhal publishing a novel 'composed on first impulse' and the several drafts of his letter to Balzac was that he knew exactly who he was sending the letter to, and second-guessing how that person might receive it – in the way that writers may adjust what they submit for prizes according to their knowledge of who the judges are. Balzac was Stendhal's senior; Stendhal wanted to get his novel to Balzac but there were difficulties: 'My janitor, by whom I wanted to send you *la Chartreuse* – as to the King of Novelists of this century – refuses to go to rue Cassini, no.1.

He pretends not to understand my instructions' (from a letter to Balzac that Stendhal signed, why not, 'Frederick'). Balzac admired the novel and wrote a generous review and Stendhal was dumbfounded and so, in writing to Balzac to thank him, stuttered. 'Who do you write *for*?' is a regular question asked in interviews with authors. Sometimes for oneself and sometimes for Balzac. I write 'for myself and strangers', said Gertrude Stein.

Like plain style, plain cooking has a perceived moral value – you can tell the goodies from the baddies by what they eat. Kitty and Levin in *Anna Karenina* make jam and pick mushrooms, while back in Moscow Oblonsky swills down oysters from Germany with French champagne. Plain cooking in novels is often associated with childhood and family and authenticity. Stephen Knight's *Mr Schnitzel* ends with a simple recipe for schnitzel sent by his mother in a letter. Carol Shields's *The Stone Diaries* includes a recipe for 'Aunt Daisy's Lemon Pudding' that is exactly the one my own mother used to cook; its appearance on the printed page of a novel surprised me, but then I realised that for generations all mothers in the Western world cooked this recipe, and this was Shields's point.

In an interview, Raymond Carver suggested that he wrote short stories because he was leading such a rackety life that novels, for which domestic stability can be helpful, were out of the question. The question being: Why do writers write in the forms they choose to write in? A problem with Carver's answer is that it sounds so reasonable. Most writers don't even know why they are writing at all. And even if they skip that question, how do they know, for example, that the sentences they are writing do not actually belong in some *other* book? Or that the novel they are writing about the First World War is not in fact about sex and drugs in the 1960s or the politics of post-Brexit Britain? It might of course be about all of these.

No, I tell Robyn, I didn't drop acid in the 60s and nor did I have lots of sex. I went on long bike rides in flat places (Lincolnshire, Holland). I was shy and conformist. I had terrible haircuts. Lots of books, not enough music. Robyn looks disappointed. I'm a little disappointed myself, but at least I'm still alive. Every counterculture needs a culture to be counter *to*, and that was my gang, and it was in the saddle (and still is), and there were more people in my gang, though the other gang was better at grabbing the headlines. Headlines can be misleading. Here is Derek Jarman responding to an interviewer's remark that 'People would expect public schools to be hives of sexual activity': 'No . . . my school was puritanical, ran on muscular Christianity punctuated by alarm bells . . . We spent most of our spare time polishing our shoes.' In any decade, a vast amount of time is spent polishing shoes and washing one's hair and oiling bicycle chains. Because history is written by the victors, the 1920s are seen now as a golden age of modernism, but during that decade far more detective novels and collections of traditional poetry were published than books by Eliot and Pound and Woolf. Right now, translations and cross-genre books are getting more attention than they used to, but you wouldn't know it from what you see people reading on the tube.

Walker Percy, 'The Man on the Train': 'There is a great deal of difference between an alienated commuter riding a train and this same commuter reading a book about an alienated commuter riding a train . . . The non-reading commuter exists in true alienation, which is unspeakable; the reading commuter rejoices in the speakability of his alienation, and in the new triple alliance of himself, the alienated character, and the author.' That was written roughly mid-last century, when alienation was hot. There's a lot of it around in that train. Someone needs to stand up and open the window.

Nor did I start a little magazine with a group of like-minded friends when I was in my twenties. I waited until I was in my sixties and started looking at the things-to-do-before-you-die lists. Swimming with dolphins, pass. *Sonofabook* ran for two issues. After the opening number I asked guest editors to choose the contents, but people closely related to each of the first three editors I hooked in started dying, and then did die, so I pulled the plug. I had rashly supposed it might last for a few more issues. Here's Tim Kendall, the editor of *Thumbscrew*, founded in 1994 as an 'antidote to a London poetry scene which appeared to outsiders as cosy, self-savouring, mediocre' – so far, so traditional – writing in its final issue in 2003: 'It may seem ironic that, having achieved sound finances, a stable subscription base, and a fairly wide reputation, *Thumbscrew* should now be killed off . . .

Thumbscrew could not risk becoming repetitive or predictable, or finding itself part of an establishment it has spent so much time mocking. Having arrived, the only decent thing to do is leave immediately.' How romantic, says Robyn – an affair, not a long-term commitment. Who is going to bring up the kids?

The thing about the famous dog, I must have got that from some interview. Dogs and writers, it makes sense: no one can spend all day sitting at a desk, and I can't see Jack jogging or going to the gym. I'd guess Jack has regular circuits: along the estuary as far as the old house that used to be the lock-keeper's, across the fields to the orphanage and back along the road. What does he think about, walking along? What does the dog think about? Are these walks when he *gets his ideas*? People often ask that, 'How do you get your ideas?', and Jack's answer is a version of the one that many writers give: 'I go for a walk.' But he may well use the walks to *get away from* his ideas, let the wind blow through him. Ideas are scary.

In a mean mood, I decide that no author should be allowed to publish more than six books: it would clear space for others to get a look-in. But every writer should be allowed to write a bad book: 'Do send us this work you need to get out of your system, although we can't absolutely promise to publish it.' No one has to read *all* the books an author has written (or any of them). There are writers I admire but whose recent work I've let pass by; I've got their flavour, and if I want that taste again I'll reread.

When an author whose books from small presses I have enjoyed moves to a big publisher, I tend to take a break. Suddenly this author is all over the place and there are headlines acclaiming her as 'the best writer you have never read'. Who is this *you*? I don't feel jilted, and I don't feel the author has sold out. She deserves this. It's more like, now that she has got all these new readers, she doesn't need me.

Rereading: Bolaño, for instance. At the time of his death at the age of fifty in 2003, just one slim book was available in English; since then, a torrent. I reread *The Secret of Evil*, which contains stories and essays and bits of what could be either, salvaged from files found on Bolaño's computer after he died. The editor found it 'difficult to decide which of the unpublished narrative texts should be regarded as finished and which are simply sketches', especially as all Bolaño's work 'seem[s] to be governed by a poetics of inconclusiveness', which is one way of putting it. Three of the texts close with images of extreme cold, as if the heating has been switched off. They don't *end*; they just stop. They are unsolved crimes; the investigation has been shut down because the leads led nowhere, and there aren't any new ones.

There is also the work (stories, poems, writing that couldn't decide what jacket or dress to wear) I *haven't* written, that got away – because it slipped off the hook when I tried to reel it in, because it didn't have the right *shape*, because it got ill, because one of the main characters wandered out to the balcony for a cigarette and never came back, because a single sentence being not quite right was telling me the whole structure was rotten, because my privacy policy wouldn't permit it, because I added too much chilli pepper, because it turned out to be not what I thought it was about and I lost the trail, or quite simply and most commonly because I wasn't a good enough writer.

Annie Dillard: 'Sometimes part of a book simply gets up and walks away. The writer cannot force it back in place. It wanders off to die.'

There are always gaps. If I can take a break from reading a certain author, the author can take a break from the reader. (Wolfgang Koeppen, after publication of his novel *Death in Rome* in 1954, discussed further novels with his publisher, and accepted advances and agreed deadlines, and died forty years later without delivering.) There was a long gap before X's new book and after – well, which one was it? Robyn will know. X's publishers must have been fingering their worry beads: readers might have forgotten all about her by the time she delivered the new one. They announced it a couple of times and then nothing, it didn't appear. This went on for years. Complete silence. What was she *doing*? Maybe there wouldn't be another book, maybe she had decided her whole writing career was a mistake, it wasn't what she was on this planet for, from now on she was going to be a lorry driver. Or an entomologist. Or she had converted to a religion that held that all books (except for *their* book) were the work of the devil. Or *we* were at fault, as readers? We had disappointed her. We had welcomed her onto the shelves as *this* kind of writer when she had been aiming for a completely different shelf. Or something much simpler, she'd gone for a walk in the woods and been eaten by a bear. (But then there'd have been a body, or at least some bones?) And then the new book did come out and everything carried on as before, back on track, and the gap closed. It was like a marriage in which one of the partners has an affair, walks out, and then one rainy Thursday morning walks back in, takes off their coat and switches on the kettle.

Does all this or any of this add up? Probably not. No one ever promised that it would. And even if it did, you'd still have to get up and go to work next day.

Robyn invited me to a reading. Seeing a writer you respect in person is rarely a good idea. You want them to be both humble and authoritative, fallible and infallible – they can't win, and neither can you. By the time I arrived Robyn had already downed three glasses of free wine. I spent a lot of the evening staring at the ceiling, the struts and beams, working out how it was held up. There was a time in my life when I wanted to be an architect. When the writer had finished the bookshop person invited questions from the audience – silence, everyone looking down at their shoes or scratching their ears, and I wanted them to hold it for longer, to see how long they dared. But then the writer said first questions are always awkward so why didn't they just skip to the second question. And someone asked her about a book she hadn't read, never mind written.

Back in 1978 Douglas Dunn was doing an event at the Riverside Studios. I liked his poetry very much – I cycled from Leeds to Hull to find Terry Street, the title of his first book – so I booked a ticket. I was expecting a man with a beard but he'd shaved it off. I was expecting poetry and the performance began with Dunn, in the words of a former artistic director of Dance Umbrella, 'going all round the studio on his back very slowly'. This was Douglas Dunn, American dancer and choreographer, born 1942, and his performance went on for an hour, in silence, and I felt I'd been taken hostage and I couldn't get up and walk out, I was in the middle of the front row, it would have been making a *point* of walking out. It would have been like saying sorry, I thought this person whose wedding or funeral I'm attending was someone else, silly me, easy mistake.

'Je est un autre': from a letter by Rimbaud. Many writers have said this – Pessoa: 'To live is to be other' – but Rimbaud's is the best-known formulation because the subject can't even command the verb and in a sentence of just four words surrenders authority. Yes, but *any* 'autre'? Or a very specific 'autre'? The guy slumped on a stool in the betting shop, surrounded by torn stubs on the floor? The point of the 'autre' is that she, he or it is unknowable until I loosen the reins on 'je'. I don't get to *choose*, though that would be nice. D. J. Enright has a poem that begins, 'I would like to be that elderly Chinese gentleman' – a man with a face 'not disfigured with fortune' dining in a Chinese restaurant with his wife and their children and grandchildren; a man 'who doesn't fret about being respected, since he is'. And another poem, a decade later, that begins, 'Another person I'd like to be / Is a 19th-century composer of / Masses for the Dead' ('With the years one's ambitions grow humbler').

I don't meet up with Robyn every day, or even every other day. I don't write or even read every day. I might click on a link and read something online, I might look for something on the shelves and not find it and pick out instead a book I read years ago and graze the opening paragraphs, I might very well do that, but no dedicated, deliberate reading. I might work on something that actually pays money and then have a long bath and think Jesus, this weather. I might think about going fishing and I might pull out the fridge instead and do some serious scrubbing. I might look at some old photographs, I might contemplate the mystery of 'Fire Doors'. I might become cat-like: kitchen, then out into the garden, then back in, then the stairs, then the bedroom, and all this shifting around for no discernible reason. I might do very little of anything, or even nothing, and I don't mean the kind of doing-nothing that in writers' talk is often billed as incubation time, absorption time, before the writing begins. Gertrude Stein: 'It takes a lot of time to be a genius. You have to sit around so much, doing nothing.' If you take that seriously – which I don't think she meant me to do, it was just a quip – it's an end-justifies-the-means argument, and doing nothing doesn't need justifying. Most people are not geniuses however much time they sit around doing nothing and most people don't write. Most people don't *read*, except for the free newspapers on public transport, and that's fine too.

Books do furnish a room, but first you need the room. How does Robyn, out of her wages as a waitress, afford not only to buy books but to roof, feed and clothe herself? Does she moonlight as a stockbroker? She tells me about the essay on the freelance life in London written by the man who sits at a table by the window in the café where she works – he has sent her a draft and it's good, she says, well written and well researched – but I'm still no wiser about her personal finances. And when she asks me if I would like to see the essay I decide they are getting on fine, these two, I'm superfluous, I'll wait until it's in print.

A man tells me that after his mother died he had to shift more than 4,000 books from the family home and Robyn is amused by my surprise that people not in the so-called literary world might own so many books, and also by my assumption – Robyn can read me – that she might be 'working on something' herself. Robyn is not going to ask if she can send me some of her writing because she *doesn't write*. Robyn is a reader. And though I might be forgiven for assuming that anyone as interested as Robyn is in reading books is also writing them, I don't think I should be forgiven. Certainly not by Robyn.

Robyn makes her own assumptions about me. When she tells me that no one needs any more novels about adultery in Hampstead, I think she assumes I live there. 'Hampstead' is shorthand for rich and white and they employ a cleaner, 'adultery' is shorthand for their having nothing to worry about except who is sleeping with who, but people who live in Hampstead are just as *real* as people who live in Hackney. The issue here isn't about 'real life'. The issue is that Hampstead is *on a hill* – higher up than Hackney, therefore less prone to flooding, therefore more expensive, and for as long as anyone can remember whole libraries of novels have been written by, for and about the people who live on the hill, and published by them too. They have 'disposable income'. For some, the Hampstead novel *is* English literature – which Ford Madox Ford reported Stephen Crane as characterising as 'one immense, petty, Parlour Game. Our books he used to say were written by men who never wanted to go out of drawing rooms for people who wanted to live at perpetual tea parties.' If Robyn is saying that we need more biodiversity, more books about the lives of those who can't afford to live on the hill, or of the people who are washing the Hampstead bedsheets and fixing the drains, then I'm with her, but don't ban books just because they happen to be set in NW3. Robyn asks me if I live in Hampstead. No. Would I like to live in Hampstead? Again no; I'm quite happy in this much cheaper district where I am. The smile on Robyn's face reads: You would say that, wouldn't you?

If we're going to cancel certain books, I suggest to Robyn, how about dystopias? The market is saturated. 'Dystopian nightmares' – because dystopian sweet dreams don't happen, except for the people who make money out of them. It's bad enough already without dystopias proclaiming it's going to get even worse, and offering guidance to those who are steering things that way. Dystopias have helped drag us down the shoddy road – the awfulness isn't so much warned against as presented as a done deal, and the characters helpless to turn things round. Has Robyn read *The Road* by Cormac McCarthy? No, but she has seen the film. OK, it's pretty faithful to the book. 'Barren, silent, godless . . . Charred and limbless trunks of trees stretching away on every side' – that's the landscape described in the opening pages of *The Road*, and we know what we're in for. You wouldn't want to go there for a holiday. It's apocalyptic. Dystopian novels are as fond of apocalypse as religions: they play upon the shifty feeling that we miserable sinners may not have lived our short lives as best we could or should have, so are due some punishment. We are both appalled by dystopias and believe we deserve them. Lowest-common-factor justice is involved: we are all guilty of something. Dystopias collude with the notion that suffering and pain – preferably the suffering and pain of others – are good for you. Dystopias stroke our fears and see a dollar sign light up and sell them back to us as entertainment. Books that *tell it as it is* can be as manipulative and escapist as any others.

Dystopias and *poshlust* are first cousins: the more the bleakness is hammered home, the more readers are persuaded that what they are reading must be *authentic*. Dystopias are often forward projections of Westerns, in which survival depends on luck and brute masculine strength. It's a handy pedigree. For men, a part of the appeal is a stupid nostalgia. Knives and guns come in handy. Women are for fucking and leaving. There is also sentimentality, bucketfuls of this. Among the quotes from reviews printed on the first pages of my paperback of McCarthy's *The Road*: 'beautiful, hypnotic and terrifyingly real'; 'the sheer, terrible beauty of the writing'; 'both terrifying and beautiful'; 'a work of such terrible beauty' – Beauty and the Beast, loving up. There is no beauty in hunger, pain, cold, fear and diarrhoea, which are the daily experience of McCarthy's father-and-son in *The Road*; nor in the collapse of societies that have struggled towards some form of decent civilisation, nor in wrecked nature. What beauty, where beauty? Not in the content, so it has to be in the fine writing – and McCarthy *is* fine, in his strong-arm way, pulling on macho biblical rhythms, though it's not a little odd that throughout both the novel and the film the son calls his dad 'Papa' like the 19th-century Victorian middle-class child in that painting used to advertise soap, which again feels sentimental, pulling on the strings.

Robyn stays quiet. I'm almost sorry. Sentimentality is not *wrong*, and if you can't be sentimental when you're young, then when? Robyn suggests: When you are old?

Pick a date, any date. Jim Jones, founder of the Peoples Temple, predicted that a nuclear holocaust would happen on 15 July 1967. While I was at school in that decade another end-of-the-world was predicted for 5 February; I don't recall the year but the date was my friend Mike's birthday, and I worried about whether before or after the cake. (Also, Mike had some status here, he had somehow been *chosen*, but neither of us could work out whether it was a status I should be jealous of.) Trouble is, the religious nutters have queered the pitch: so many of their deadlines have slipped by that many now find it hard to believe the science-based predictions. We're not like the others, say the climatologists, and they really aren't, but we've heard that one before too.

Happiness is hard. In *Memoirs of an Egotist*, Stendhal decided not to write about the times when he was happiest because he was afraid of 'deflowering' them: 'I'll skip them instead.' In *The Charterhouse of Parma* he did get happiness onto the page – the recipe included incarceration, bliss and Italian sunlight – but for most writers it's a devil. Music takes happiness in its stride – music *thrives* on happiness, music can *create* happiness – so why not literature? Partly because after words got printed in books the whole business became solitary rather than communal. (There was a trade-off – in place of collective joy we got new pleasures of the text – but neither of the negotiating teams came out of this well.) Partly because of the reluctance of those committees of readers who recommend to other readers what they should be reading to take happiness seriously as a literary subject: the prizes go to blood, toil, tears and sweat; and to grief and dystopias. Poetry can do happiness better than prose fiction – as in the relaxed, convivial poems of many of the New York School poets – and twenty years ago happiness was one of the things I was trying to get into my own poetry: otherwise, what was the point? I was bored with doom, the *exquisite* doominess that is the default mode of, in particular, the thing called literary fiction. Somewhere in William Golding – I think it's in *Free Fall*; I remember the line because it was shocking – there is this: 'Happiness is a five-finger exercise.' Is happiness child's play, less *grown up* than accepting that life is a vale of tears full stop? That's a cop-out. 'Happiness writes white' is also a cop-out. Happiness is far too important to be left to the hacks who write greetings-card verses. If literature can't cope with it don't blame happiness.

Coming out of an 'in conversation' event with an American writer in the middle of the afternoon, we blink in the sudden sunlight. It's as if we are surfacing from one of those indie films set in Brooklyn in which the characters navigate confusion and despair with such articulacy you wonder how they ever got confused in the first place. How do they do it, over there? We can't even match their production values. Their whole package is better – place names, cars, trucks, landscapes, accents, slang, music, graffiti – or is it just the films and books that have persuaded me of this? The man asking the questions sat with his arms folded across his belly while the writer took off. She reads so widely and thinks about the issues so intelligently, how does she ever find the time to *write*? At the end, Robyn and I looked at the queue to buy her book and decided we didn't need it: after hearing her talk, the book would have been just a souvenir programme.

Robyn has sketched out a plan for a Hampstead novel. Twin sisters sex-trafficked from Eastern Europe escape from their abuser and knock on the door of a retired librarian who is archiving the papers of his recently deceased neighbour, a Romanian mathematician who may or may not have been the twins' long-lost grandfather. The librarian's wife is living with a group of squatters occupying a derelict mansion on the Bishops Avenue owned by a Russian oligarch. A leopard has escaped from London Zoo. The Thames has broken its banks and the floodwaters have reached the Holloway Road. Every Sunday afternoon the librarian stands in the driveway of the house in the Bishops Avenue where his wife is living, sets the alarm on his phone and weeps for fifteen minutes. I tell Robyn that on paper it seems fine. Robyn blanks. When anyone says something looks good *on paper*, they have precious little faith that it's going to work in practice.

A friend of Robyn – true story – has copies of all of Jack Robinson's books, which her boyfriend had acquired for her. By 'acquired' she means shoplifted. Books are *designed* to be shoplifted – flat, light, pocket-sized, and they don't rustle. Much easier than bottles of wine or packets of crisps. All of Jack's books except *An Overcoat*, and it was while the boyfriend was walking out of the shop with that one that he was nabbed by a security guard. They prosecuted, and Robyn's friend was in court when her boyfriend was asked if he had anything to say for himself and he said he'd like all Robinson's other titles to be taken into consideration. Suspended sentence. She was so proud of him.

Robyn has had an idea. Low-level, but they all count. At the literary festivals, after an event there are always two queues: one for the toilets, one for the authors who are sitting at a table signing their books. Smile and sign, smile and sign, or the other one. They should combine the two, Robyn suggests; it would be much more efficient. She is onto something. If you have to queue for one thing and then join another queue for the other thing, many people choose the more urgent thing and skip the other. The desks where the authors sign their books would need to be outside the toilets, or if it's raining maybe *in* the toilets. If it comes down to a choice between the Ladies and the Gents, toss a coin.

What happens next? At a crossroads, Samuel Beckett's Mercier and Camier toss their umbrella in the air – it falls like 'a great wounded bird' – to decide which way to go. In Robert Louis Stevenson's *The Master of Ballantrae*, the Master also favours 'the arbitrament of chance'. In July 1745 one of the two sons of the house of Durisdeer will ride to join Bonnie Prince Charlie, but which? They toss a coin. After the battle of Culloden, the Master and an Irish colonel toss a coin to decide 'whether we were to cut each other's throats or be sworn friends'. Wandering in the wilderness in North America, 'Ballantrae often decided on our course by spinning a coin' – '"I know no better way," said he, "to express my scorn of human reason."' His companions surely knew that the coin belonged to RLS and had a head on both sides.

It's raining. Robyn takes me along the corridor leading to the toilets at the back of the café and opens the triangular door of a small understairs cupboard – a broom cupboard, except that it contains not brooms but umbrellas left behind by customers. They look like small animals huddled together in a cage at the zoo. How long have they been here? I ask

Robyn, and she shrugs and tells me to take my pick. There are also two scarves, a bobble hat and a doll with only one eye. I think one of the umbrellas may belong to Kafka's Karl Rossmann, who left it on board ship when he disembarked in New York – and after asking a friend to guard his suitcase, which contained among other things a clean white shirt and a salami packed by his mother and which he had only nibbled at during the voyage from Hamburg, went back to retrieve but got involved instead with the ship's stoker and then in an argument with the captain and the chief cashier and a man named Schubal and then discovered his long-lost uncle, who took him home, and neither umbrella nor suitcase is heard of again – but I don't know which. I think I'll just leave these umbrellas here, I tell Robyn. It's probably only a shower.

Walking in the Hebrides in my mid-teens with a group of other campers, we were surprised by a thunderstorm and took shelter in an abandoned croft. There were Penguin crime books on a shelf, the green ones. I read *The Postman Always Rings Twice*, cover to cover, while the storm raged outside, and even if the postman had hammered on the door or shouted through the broken window I wouldn't have heard.

There's no need for a *next* book by Jack. Robyn disagrees: she has taken out a lifetime subscription, she has made an investment, Jack can't just stop. I waver. It's nice to have Jack there, being busy. And then, having said that, I think how cosy this is: Jack writing in his room, trees outside the window, central heating, books on shelves and on the floor too, family (if family) tiptoeing around those books on the floor, big scruffy dog he walks with along the estuary, late afternoons, and Robyn and all the other Robyns buying every other book he writes, a level of trust having been established here, and the publisher middle-managing between them, the erudite editor, the keen young folk in publicity, the expense-account lunches, the cover roughs for approval, and the bookshops with their 'staff picks' and their upscale stationery, the Moleskines, the Pantone mugs, the *customer service*. On Twitter and Facebook the likes, the *can't waits*, the assumption that we're all on the same page. That we are *we*. Robyn shrugs. I'm just fussing about the packaging, she says. I'm not so sure. Something is being *perpetrated* here. Hasn't Jack got better things to do? Haven't I?

The 'same page' that 'we' assume we are on is often a page in the *Guardian*, one of the house journals of my tribe which we comfortably grumble about. On Saturdays we sit in cafés with our flat whites and our smashed avocados sticking pins into hand-made scale models of writers we agree to dislike. That we in turn are disliked by some of the locals, who throw empty beer cans at our tables as they pass by, bolsters our feeling of solidarity.

So much bile and bigotry . . . I stay clear of the comments posted below online pieces on bookish matters, I tell Robyn. She, on the other hand, is a connoisseur. She especially likes the ones under the art reviews: civilisation has gone to the dogs. The commenters hark back to a mythical time when paintings looked like whatever they were paintings *of* and poetry rhymed and Britannia ruled the waves. They feel they are being taken for a ride. There's a conspiracy, and the reviewer must be in someone's pay. So much pent-up anger spilling out, you could run the country on that energy. People *have* harvested that energy: political careers are made out of it. But do I want, Robyn asks, to go back to a time when Sir Arthur Posh-Bottomley pronounced on a book and everyone doffed their caps and nodded?

I do worry about the packaging. Packaging is engulfing the Earth. Packaging is designed to sell things and competes with other packaging to attract attention. Packaging includes the marketing campaign a book is wrapped in, and when more money is spent on that than on the book itself then the book *becomes* its packaging. Robyn will ask me how I'm supposed to know a book even exists if I'm not told about it; I'll ask in return how I'm supposed to know one from another if they are all so wonderful. I stand at the table in the bookshop on which the newborn books are laid out in rows and feel not just apprehension but dismay: how can they all possibly live up to the expectations?

Look, there, at the table by the door – that's Billy Bob Thornton, isn't it? Robyn is doubtful. Why would Billy Bob Thornton be sitting in a café in London on a rainy Tuesday? But the weather has got nothing to do with it. That man is the barber in *The Man Who Wasn't There*, who is Billy Bob Thornton, and he's got to have his coffee *somewhere*, doesn't he? I watch him fiddling with his phone and am pleased to see that he is left-handed. Robyn reminds me that the film was made almost twenty years ago, so by now that barber's hair would be twenty shades more grey; and secondly, that actors don't necessarily look like the characters they play in films – they are *actors*. When we look back to the table by the door, Billy Bob has gone.

I'm sorry Billy Bob has left because I'd have liked to ask him about the parallels between *The Man Who Wasn't There* and *The Postman Always Rings Twice*. In the Coen Brothers' film, Ed Crane – the character played by Billy Bob – gets away with one murder but is convicted of another that he didn't commit. In James M. Cain's novel Frank Chambers gets away with one murder but is convicted of another that he didn't commit. While they are on death row, both characters write down their versions of what has happened – Ed for a men's magazine that's paying him 5 cents a word, Frank writing the book we're coming to the end of (though he's relying on the prison chaplain to 'look it over and show me the places where maybe it ought to be fixed up a little, for punctuation and all that'). They are very different characters. Frank has a raging sexual appetite, Ed is a perpetual bystander: 'I didn't see anyone. No one saw me. I was the barber.' Writing is not going to save either of them from the noose or the electric chair, so *why*? Out of a need for some kind of justice, I think, a justice different from that of the legal system and which for better or worse they associate with the written word.

The killer collared for the wrong crime, usually one of which he is innocent, is a trope. There are also writers who have won literary prizes for the *wrong book*.

The narratives of both Cain's novel and the Coen Brothers' film echo the 'True Confessions' of prisoners awaiting execution that found an eager market in the early 18th century and jump-started the English novel. Jack Sheppard's first-person account of his robberies and his several escapes from prison ('as told' to Daniel Defoe) has everything: true crime, Houdini-like breakouts from chains and manacles, love interest, betrayals, kindness to an elderly mother and an abiding concern with 'justice'. Sheppard deplores the professional thief-catchers, living off their profits from blackmail and racketeering, who 'deserve the gallows as richly as any of the thieves'. He is telling his tale, he insists, 'to satisfy the curious, and do justice to the innocent'. For readers, even those who knew that words were put into the mouths of the condemned men and women by their ghostwriters, Sheppard's words gained authority from being spoken 'on the brink of eternity'. Aged 22, Sheppard was hanged in November 1724; a third of the population of London followed his progress from Newgate in an open cart to the gallows at Tyburn.

An author I admire has had her early novels reissued with new covers. They've changed the insides too. I've been rereading one of the novels with its sparky new cover design and episodes that I recall taking up large sections of the book have shrunk. The scene in a back garden in south London, for example, in April or May, all the summer to come, with the characters just chilling, talking about food and work and sex and death, no scoring of plot points – I remember that scene lasting for a whole afternoon and it's over in a page and a half. Some things that I remember aren't there at all.

'He remembers that on this avenue they climbed into a taxi, but nothing about the drive.' That's from Mavis Gallant's story 'The Ice Wagon Going Down the Street'. I remember a damp flat in Geneva with a trunk not fully unpacked, and a party somewhere glitzy in a snowstorm, and an episode involving a man and a woman called Agnes – not sexual ('Nothing *happened*') but so revelatory that the man will never speak about it to his wife. Rereading, I find I'd forgotten that the taxi driver gets paid twice, and that this reminds the man of a 'theory concerning North American behavior' that he'd heard from someone else, but not Gallant's distinctive way of putting all of these things on the page, both capacious and fiercely compressed, and I still don't know how she does it.

A trope: the stranger in the bar or the bus station in the middle of nowhere to whom the narrator bares their soul, because they'll never see each other again ('an ear without repercussions', as Edouard Levé puts it). The soul is usually male, the passive listener female. It's a framing device, as in Alfred Hayes's *In Love*, which is the story of a wrecked life told over afternoon cocktails in a hotel bar: 'Odd, though, the man said to the pretty girl, how I sleep well, how unimpaired my appetite is, and yet I seem always tired now . . .' And as in *The Rime of the Ancient Mariner*: 'He holds him with his glittering eye – / The Wedding-Guest stood still, / And listens like a three years' child: / The Mariner hath his will.' It's a form of imprisonment, the victim subdued if not erased by the storytelling skills of the narrator.

Another trope: unable to sleep, a child comes downstairs and sees or overhears something that . . . I have a hunch that children feature more often in fiction by women. They dramatise a lack of agency: along with old people and animals, children have very little of this, and nor until about yesterday did women.

Book covers I have a soft spot for are those from the 1940s and 50s that packaged classics, often translated ones, as pulp fiction. Zola and Balzac, being French and therefore obsessed with sex, got this treatment often: décolletage, dishevelled hair, rumpled bedsheets and post-coital cigarettes. There was something innocent in the cynicism on display here, and there is something much less innocent in the more recent retro pulp-fiction covers. Later, publishers favoured fine-art reproductions for the classics – gentrifying, shifting them into a more up-market, less rowdy part of town.

The experience of revisiting cities remembered with affection almost always turns out badly and fiction treats it cruelly. Asher in Alfred Hayes' *The End of Me* pays his young cousin to walk with him through the New York he remembers: 'The weather of long ago. The menus of dead chefs. Assignations in taxis since junked and scrapped . . . Christ: what was I in, the resurrection business?' In Buenos Aires, a former girlfriend of the narrator in Edgardo Cozarinsky's 'The Sentimental Journey': 'What you recall doesn't matter to anybody. If I let you talk, you're capable of mentioning Pasaje Seaver . . . If anybody remembers it, it's to give a sigh of relief it doesn't exist anymore . . . So get it into your head: I don't remember. *You* remember – if you want to. Now, please, get out.'

Travelling into and out of cities by rail, I see houses not as they pose for the streets but before they've shaved or put on their make-up: tatty back gardens, rusting fire escapes, rain-puddled trampolines in muddy gardens, improvised party spaces on the roofs of cowboy extensions, compost, mulch, everything unkempt. A woman leans far out, smoking, from a window in a flat in which she's not allowed to smoke. A man steps out of the shower. How many books are being written, one keystroke after another, in back rooms and bad light, that I'll never know about? It's all *evidence* of something, and observing it feels like an invasion of privacy.

Photographs of readers also make me a voyeur. The photos in *On Reading* by André Kertész show readers in parks, gardens, the street, a classroom, bookshops, trains, libraries, balconies, churches, a bed, a fire escape and, spectacularly, rooftops – all of them unaware they are being observed. C. K. Williams wrote a sequence of poems about readers that includes a man pausing to read a scrap of newspaper while retrieving a spare wheel from the boot of his car, a one-year-old child who 'stares importantly' at a page of Le Monde before tearing it into pieces and eating them ('a delicious editorial on unemployment and recession, a tasty jeu de mots on government ineptitude'), a man in the subway and a woman on a bus who raises her eyes from her book and looks directly at the poet – 'she must have felt me thinking about her'.

Knighthoods can be revoked. Saints can be removed from the liturgical calendar. There are authors (including many dead ones) who, if invited to read at the student union, would have to be escorted through a crowd protesting their racist, sexist or fascist tendencies, sometimes all three. Does being a good writer get you a pass on being a lousy human being? (No.) Robyn is among the protesters, but is herself at risk of being outlawed. The authors must be challenged but she doesn't want to eject them from the campus: there are good people who write badly, there are bad people who can write very well, and we should be able to handle this. If we allow that writers can make mistakes – and we have to, because otherwise we wouldn't have anything to read – then we have also to allow that some of those mistakes will be big ones. Others among the protesters believe that inviting the authors lends credibility to their crass opinions, so ban them. There's a righteousness here that makes Robyn uneasy. Me too, I tell her. None of us is squeaky clean, and a book can be complicated by the reader's prejudices as well as the writer's. And that makes Robyn uneasy too: it sounds so damned reasonable, and about some of the opinions of these authors there is nothing reasonable at all, and in dealing with the toxic fall-out of those opinions where did being reasonable ever get us? 'Be reasonable' is what we're told by people who want us to agree with them.

'Whatever he looked like at that first moment it was not like a writer': Theodora Bosanquet recalling her first meeting with Henry James, who at the end of that meeting offered her employment as his 'literary amanuensis'/transcriber. 'He might perhaps have been some species of disguised cardinal, or even a Roman nobleman amusing himself by playing the part of a Sussex squire.' (If not a disguised cardinal or a Roman nobleman, what *does* a writer look like?) Bosanquet took dictation from James from 1907 until his death in 1916, working at a Remington typewriter in a green-panelled room – or in summer in the garden room – at Lamb House in Rye and sometimes in London (though not at the Reform Club, where James often stayed, which refused to admit women). Between the hours of 10.15 and around a quarter to two in the afternoon, Bosanquet fulfilled 'my function as the medium between the spoken and the written word'. James had begun the practice of dictating his novels in the 1890s, after developing a wrist sprain. His first transcriber was a young Scotsman, but women came cheaper. Seated before the Remington – 'other kinds sounded different notes; and it was almost impossibly disconcerting for him to dictate to something that made no responsive sound at all' – while James perambulated around the room, pausing only to stand 'by a bookcase or chimney-piece tall enough for him to support his arms on it' while he 'audibly pursued' a fugitive word, Bosanquet became integral to the development of James's late style, characterised by Ford Madox Ford as 'copious, involved, labyrinthine talk'. Bosanquet: 'He perfectly recognised the effect on himself; to a certain extent he even deplored it. "I tend," he once said, "to be too diffuse when I'm dictating." He found, however, that dictation was not only an easier but also a more inspiring method of composition than writing with his own hand, and considered that the increased facility more than made up for any loss of concision . . . The final form is not so pretty, but it is ever so much more alive.'

The Stendhal quotation about lottery tickets is from the translation by David Ellis of *Memoirs of an Egotist* (1832) published by Chatto & Windus. I bought my copy in a second-hand bookshop in Hammersmith in the early 1980s and it set off an obsession (many poems, and eventually a novel based on an episode in Stendhal's life). Bored and lonely in the small Italian port of Civitavecchia, where he was serving as French consul, Stendhal began writing the book on 20 June 1832 and stopped, mid-paragraph, thirteen days later in the middle of a heat wave ('It's become too hot to think'). It's a slip of a thing, barely over a hundred pages, but it takes in politics, humiliations, botched affairs, other people's salaries, preferred methods of suicide, horse-riding, apples, insults, art, stupidity, battles, reading, happiness, love, gossip, rain, oblivion . . . Who *were* these people he writes about, why should I care how much money they had, and why does he repeatedly get his basic chronology in a twist? I had no idea but I was bewitched.

The translation of the Stendhal book was commissioned by
D. J. Enright while he was an editor at Chatto. It sold poorly,
he wrote to me, but more than another book he commissioned
whose entire stock was burned in a warehouse fire. I knew
Enright, a little, because in Cairo in 1977 I bought a copy of
his first book of poems, *Season Ticket*, published in Alexandria
in 1948, for the original cover price (5 piastres), and I wrote to
him when I came back to London. We met occasionally on the
District line tube during the morning rush hour, he travelling
in to Chatto and me to my job with another publisher:
awkward chitchat while strap-hanging. Once, boarding a train
at King's Cross, I was taking my copy of his *Collected Poems*
out of my bag when I noticed that Enright was sitting in the
seat behind me, lighting his pipe. He signed the book for me,
and then I moved to another carriage; I assumed he had been
expecting privacy. The last of Enright's late commonplace
books, published posthumously, quoted from one of my poems
in a passage on misprints ('public hair', 'streets-weepers').
It occurs to me now that I was to Enright as Robyn, here,
very roughly – the distance between Enright's reading and
intelligence and my own is a country mile – is to me.

Of course Stendhal was interested in money. An ambitious
boy from the provinces with no inherited wealth, he was
sufficiently corrupted to like the opera, fine wines and good
company, and was continually in need of a job. In novels,
money tends either to be in short supply, in which case the
getting of it plays a major part in the plot; or it's there in
plentiful amounts but its origins are left vague.

Once you have taken one pen name, why not another? And then another and another? Pessoa took around seventy pen names, Stendhal's ran into the hundreds. They were usernames for different accounts for which you then forget the passwords. In his essay 'Pseudonymous Stendhal', Jean Starobinski argued that Stendhal (itself a pen name) wanted to become 'not just *an* other but *several* others' – that is, continual metamorphosis. Something sexual is involved here, both surrender and command. Stendhal lived for most of his life in hotels and rented rooms; he was always getting into a stagecoach and setting off for somewhere else; his multiplying pseudonyms are just one strand in a strategy that also involved publishing books with prefaces that disclaimed his authorship, marginalia written in code and plots laced with conspiracies and disguises, swerves and digressions, a normal day at the office.

The trouble with telling lies, I'm told, is that it gets easier after the first time and can become habitual. But what doesn't?

No one steps twice into the same book. Although all the books on my shelves have been read *by the same reader*, that reader is as fickle as any author. Rereading my old Penguin edition of Lawrence's *The Rainbow* with my name and a date, 1970, on the fly leaf, I want to rub out many of the pencilled underlinings and make new ones in different paragraphs. Starobinski named 'instability, awkwardness, and error' as the defining characteristics of Stendhal's life, but he didn't have a monopoly on those. The only people of whom we demand absolute consistency are characters in novels, in the interests of, oddly, 'realism'.

Two bearded men at a nearby table are glancing in our direction. They don't look friendly. They probably read true crime, I say. Robyn reproves me: they probably think we read self-improvement books. Life on the streets is a continual class war: the genre crowd scorned by the literary fiction crowd, the lit fic crowd scorned by the Becketteers, performance poets scorned by page poets, small-press writers scorned by those from the big hitters, and always the scorn running both ways . . . Even behind the heavy doors of Bloomsbury and Mayfair with their polished brass fittings, knives are kept sharp: the Proust gang despises the Henry James gang despises the D. H. Lawrence gang, and you can be banished from the Proust gang for reading the wrong translation. Graphic novelists and comic artists hide in the hills and make guerrilla raids. Mind how you go.

Henry James: '*January 22d* [1879]. I heard some time ago, that Anthony Trollope had a theory that a boy might be brought up to be a novelist as to any other trade. He brought up – or attempted to bring up – his own son on this principle, and the young man became a sheep-farmer, in Australia.'

Watching an author respond in public to a bad review of their book is like watching a tennis match. Episodes that migrate out of the letters column or the reviews supplement and into the news pages are even more fun: look, the literary life is *important*. Sexual escapades, current or long ago; contested wills; revelations by judges of prizes . . . Robyn shakes her head. Don't I realise how childish this is? We are interested in literature only when a writer trips on a banana skin. Or maybe wins a prize or gets a gong from the Palace. The British relate to their writers much as they do to small animals – when they pee on the neighbour's geraniums, when they drink and take drugs, how cute! Ideas, yes, as long as they stay on the shelves. Barthes in 'The Writer on Holiday' writes of 'the glamorous status which bourgeois society liberally grants its spiritual representatives (as long as they remain harmless)'. It is infantile. And how can writers complain that they are not respected within the culture when they collude in this, giggling at the back of the classroom? Robyn orders another coffee. She's a Young Turk. I'm staring hard at her forehead.

No, not a Young Turk. Often, Robyn is *older* than me. She has my years plus her own and I have only mine, and they're running out. When I assume she's thinking what I'm thinking she's thinking about something different, and more.

Robyn's bike has been found – by me. It was chained to a railing outside the house in Marchmont Street with the blue plaque telling passers-by that William Empson lived here. I recognised the bike immediately. I phoned Robyn and also the police. I bought another lock from a hardware shop and secured the bike with this second lock so that whoever removed the first lock couldn't just ride off. Everyone arrived

together – Robyn, two policemen and a man called Billy.
The police asked Robyn to prove the bike was hers, and she
showed them a photo of herself riding it. Billy said he had
bought the bike a week ago from a man called Jack. Could
he tell the police anything more about this Jack – his phone
number, his address, what he looked like? He couldn't. Jack
was just a man he met in a pub. And then Billy threw in
the towel: he unlocked his own chain and walked away, a
man with a lock with nothing to lock up, and the policemen
shrugged and Robyn took her bike.

When I see a blue plaque on a house telling me a writer once
lived there I always look through the window, expecting to
see . . . In August 2016 I did see Henri Beyle, aka Stendhal,
in Notting Hill. He was wearing sunglasses and an overcoat
– the same outfit in which he travelled in disguise to Volterra
in 1819 – and had a flower-patterned tote bag slung over his
shoulder. He looked like a brigand. As mentioned in Jack
Robinson's *An Overcoat*, he crossed the street at the lights
and I took a photograph of him on the other side of the road.
Robyn looks as if I'd told her I believe in reincarnation.

'Bracing wit' – Robyn is quoting a blurb. I think 'bracing'
means 'invigorating', like the air off the sea when you are
walking along the cliffs. Robyn detects something defensive
here, as in 'They braced themselves.'

Heads in clouds, heads buried in the sand – either way, the heads of readers are widely viewed as not being at the correct level. Heads not screwed on right . . . Clichés are landfill, less language than what language has left behind; idioms are more strange, and for children who still believe that grown-ups mean exactly what they say, they can be frightening. Aged around five, when I was told by a teacher that she had eyes in the back of her head, I asked how she could see through her hair. If in Copenhagen, say, or Düsseldorf or Bukhara, there was a museum of idioms from different languages and cultures, I'd go there at the drop of a hat. A comprehensive museum would need to be as big as the town it was located in; I'll settle for an eccentrically curated selection at an address in a side street in the suburbs, with unpredictable opening hours.

Robyn: Do you ever dream about characters in a novel? Do you ever dream that *you* are a character in a novel? I dreamt I was taking part in a re-enactment of a scene from a novel I'd been reading. The woman rigging up the lighting was wearing dungarees. Every time I got near her Robyn appeared, asking me to fill in some kind of questionnaire, and the lighting woman would run off with her slather of cables, though not before winding them round my legs and tripping me up. We were all sweating under those lights, we had a deadline to meet. The author of the novel was directing us from behind a glass window like they used to have in recording studios, using sign language, but she looked more like she was cleaning the window. We were crawling under the stage, scraping elbows, undoing buckles, the woman was wearing nothing under the dungarees, then Robyn again with her clipboard. I woke up. I looked for my copy of the novel but couldn't even remember its title.

The book that Robyn thought would win the prize has done so. Out of a sense of obligation – to whom? – I have read it. The reviews were right – it does 'speak to our present sense of crisis', etc. – and I was right too: it is itself a part of the crisis it tells us about, it is infected with *poshlust*. Robyn spreads her hands and leans forward. She tells me that if I'm judging books by criteria laid down by a dead rich white man who lived in a posh hotel in Switzerland – if I think these are the *only* criteria – if I think people historically excluded from the whole business of books have to write in accordance with rules set by those who have done the excluding – if I think 'literature' is some form of rarefied entity that exists quite apart from the society in which it is produced – if I think that the literary gatekeepers are any more trustworthy than investment bankers – and if I think what she's telling me is just a set of fashionable opinions trending on social media – then I am missing out on a *lot*.

Pause. We look at each other: old man, young woman. Later we might joke about this but right now we are inhabiting our roles: she's the person who says these things, I'm the person they're said to. We have to find a way of working here with grace and kindness and we will do, but now the scene is rolling it's hard to stop. Robyn asks: Do I know how much energy it takes, daily, 24/7, for someone who has been ignored to gain any presence at all in a scene that has incorporated into its whole practice the habit of looking through them, or away? Robyn asks: Do I talk to the other people in the bus queue or do I just listen in for the cute overheard phrase? Robyn adds: And if I hold the opinions I do about literature and still somehow manage to think of myself as a liberal, left-leaning guy . . . Robyn adds: And if I think parading all this in a book with her in there as a foil lets me off the hook . . . I get the bill.

It's not that simple: I have to catch the eye of a busy waiter, I may even have to walk to the counter . . . Another thing, Robyn says. Somewhere back in these pages I mentioned the pipe-smoking white men who wrote the critical books I read when I was a student. Have I looked in the mirror recently? If there's a difference, it's that they believed that books were culturally important and could transform lives, and I seem to be sitting on the fence. It can't be comfortable, sitting astride a thin bit of wood. If this is because the hype has been getting to me – the filler pieces, the waffle about books being 'therapy for the soul' – then I have a very thin skin. If it's because I feel let down, living in a country which despite all the great books is still mean and racist and whose political system is not fit for purpose, then I have a very simplistic notion of the relationship between books and society. If it's because I don't want my life to be changed, then I'm a little too snug in my book-lined study. What are those books doing there, on the shelves? Insulation? Have I dusted them off, recently?

Oh, and given that I went to the small trouble of inventing a pen name, why didn't I push a little harder and inhabit a Jack who was more than just me with a different name tag? The suggestion here – not an accusation, this is not a court of law – is that I used Jack as time off, a holiday from being me. 'Being me' is hard, everyone needs time off. But Jack hardly bothered even to be Jack, he spent much of his time folding his reading of other writers into tidy collages and letting *them* do the heavy lifting. I may be doing the same here, Robyn suspects.

At the end of James Buchan's *Slide*, a short, fierce novel about the stultifying endurance of privilege, the protagonist – Oxford, Foreign Office, banking – reflects that if the episodes in his life he's recounted had played out differently, if certain people had not died or gone off or been killed, he might not be standing in this particular field in Dorset, 'in this ridiculous landscape', but he would 'still be I, Richard Verey, thirty-five years old, an Englishman of the upper middle class'. Walking away under an assumed name, I was never going to get far. Reinvention is not on the cards.

At the door of the café Robyn pauses, frowning, as if she's thought of something else she wants to say, but then shakes her head and leaves. Argument is exhausting. 'Being me' is exhausting. I go to the toilet. I have a long tube journey ahead of me.

S till in the Gents, I look at myself in the mirror above
the washbasin. We grin at each other. 'Hi, Jack.' The
man at the next basin pretends to not hear: like pen names,
metafiction can make readers suspicious. In their jointly
written story about Franz Kafka working as a Hollywood
screenwriter for Frank Capra, Jonathan Lethem suggests to
Carter Scholz that they should include their own notes to
each other, and Scholz replies: 'That makes me uneasy. Where
do we stop? Calling the artifice into question requires further
metamorphoses, and once you start the process, there's no
burrow to hide in.' So much smoke, so many mirrors. But it's
too late now: they are already on the page. Lethem tells his co-
writer to lighten up: 'It's only a short story.'

My granny used to say, when she saw me getting teary
over a film we were watching on TV, 'It's only a story.'
When Robyn's bike was stolen and I offered sympathy,
she responded, 'It's only money.' A woman once said to
me, grinning from ear to ear, 'It's only sex.' To someone
despairing of the judges' decision, I want to say, 'It's only a
book.' But it is never *only* anything.

Delmore Schwartz, 'In Dreams Begin Responsibilities':
'The old lady next to me pats me on the shoulder and says,
"There, there, all of this is only a movie, young man, only a
movie," but I look up once more at the terrifying sun and the
terrifying ocean, and being unable to control my tears, I get
up and go to the men's room, stumbling over the feet of the
other people seated in my row.'

Another mirror, this one from Stendhal's *The Red and the
Black*: 'A novel is a mirror travelling down a road. Sometimes
it reflects the blue of the heavens to the eye, sometimes the
mud of the filthy puddles on the road.' Readers who are
offended should blame not the messenger but 'the inspector
of roads who lets the water gather and the muddy puddles
collect'. As a definition, or defence, of 'realism' in fiction,
this is nonsense. Roads are bumpy, mirrors are difficult
things to hold steady, and just when things are starting to get
interesting the light fades. Stendhal knew this; he inserted
this bit of cut-price theory not in a letter or memoir or review
but in a *novel*. Just a couple of paragraphs earlier he has told
the reader that the character of Mathilde – who is in love
and trying to persuade herself that she is not – 'is completely
imaginary' ('*toute à fait d'imagination*'), no mirrors involved
here at all.

About notebooks again. One page before the passage in *The
Red and the Black* in which Stendhal assures his readers that
the character of Mathilde is imaginary and two pages before
he insists that novels involve no imagination, Mathilde is

'randomly sketching with her pencil on a page in her album'. She gets Julien to a T: 'I have made his portrait without meaning to.' She goes to her room, shuts the door and 'applied herself in earnest, trying seriously to do a portrait of Julien – but without success; the portrait sketched at random remained the best likeness'.

And a mirror in a notebook: 'Girl at mirror arranging her hair severely, twisting it like a mechanic tightening part of an engine.' That's from the top of the handwritten page reproduced on the dust jacket of Murray Bail's *Notebooks 1970–2003*. Bail's notebooks are cousin to those of many other writers: observations ('She cleaned her teeth vigorously, the way she tore open envelopes'), ideas for stories, the curious lives of others (the woman dying in a hospice in Sydney who had sold flowers to Matisse in Nice), quotations (Steinberg: 'When I look at a scene in the countryside, I see a signature in the lower right-hand corner'), overheard snatches of conversation ('He had a pathological hatred of – what was it? – butter'), notable accomplishments ('He invented a cough'), useful advice ('When coming to rest in an avalanche, dribble to see which way is up'), transcriptions of newspaper reports (a thief who each time he robbed left behind a shirt stolen in a previous burglary) . . . Isn't this just one damn thing after another? Readers who admire Bail's fiction might be interested, but why anyone else? Because notebooks' licence to face in at least four different directions on a single page affords an openness that more focused forms of writing – novels, stories – trade away for narrative momentum. They admit self-doubt (Bail: 'As you can see, I'm not very good at this – whatever this is'). Digressions (from what?) are their soul. Yehuda Amichai: 'If we are trained well, we can do three or four things at the same time: ride in a car, cry, and look through a window; eat, love, think. And all the time consciousness passes like an elevator among the floors.' A notebook, not a novel, is Stendhal's mirror travelling down a road, reflective on both sides; or it is Amichai's elevator, rising and falling among the floors.

Robyn – a little pedantically, I think – says that Stendhal's mirror-along-a-road is as wrong for notebooks as it is for novels, because roads lead from somewhere to somewhere else and notebooks do nothing of the kind. Instead of progressing, something cumulative happens: echoes, repetitions . . . Bail: 'Writing: a form of dark vegetation (spreading).'

We're more than halfway. Why does the journey back always seem shorter than the journey there? Why do the pages of a book turn faster towards the end? Where did last week go? Why are afternoons – which in childhood lasted for ever – so short? Why is a book that was published only a year ago now past its sell-by date, unavailable in any bookshop? Why do we keep on having to 'rediscover' writers who wrote and published and died within my lifetime? Why is it already after midnight? Why do I have this sense of, I don't know, *occlusion*, without even knowing what the word means? On the other hand, in the care home where I visit a woman who ran a tiny bookshop in Notting Hill for nearly half a century, the tea is weak and pale and time has slowed to the pace of an insect crawling across a page. I'm saving up *In Search of Lost Time* for when I get to the care home myself. A friend tells me that she read Proust in her twenties, when she was living in a small town where she knew very few people and her marriage was on the rocks, and when she got to the end she turned back to volume one and started again. I read Dostoevsky and a whole shelf of fat black Penguin Classics in translation when I was at Cambridge, a period in my life I have few fond memories of. Very long books are often read by people at times when they are unhappy and perhaps lonely.

When I was aged around twelve my mother took me to a library to learn how to use reference books, which pre-Google she had no reason not to believe was going to be a life skill: gather information from different sources, recognise bias, make connections, be intelligent. Later, I worked on reference books myself, including the first edition of the Collins English Dictionary: men, mostly, writing the definitions, and an all-female 'typing pool'. And I wrote for and edited a 24-volume History of the World; the books were mailed monthly to subscribers, plush large-format books that asked to be displayed on coffee tables, the coffee tables which have survived from that pre-internet era with only a few minor scuffs and which now support interior design magazines and catalogues of art exhibitions sponsored by Swiss banks.

There's no mystery about publishing, any more than there is about running a stall in the market. Buy in a product that people will want, present it in an attractive way, price it reasonably, shout in the street. All the jargon – backlists and frontlists and second serial rights – is beside the point. As with banking and politics and window-cleaning, no need for professional qualifications. There is rarely anything 'risk-taking' about it. It's not brain surgery. People can die from brain surgery; no one dies from not being published, or from being published badly. It's not even expensive: you can publish a book for less money than many people spend on their summer holidays. And Robyn tells me it's easy for *me* to say that: I'm on the inside. For anyone on the outside who has written and now wants to publish, it can feel like getting on a plane to a country with a different language, currency, even the noise made by the ambulance sirens. And I reply: The articles that claim to 'demystify' publishing serve only to increase mystification. As with explanations of how to achieve a healthy lifestyle, people come away worried that they've missed a bit, or happy with their new bits of know-how but unsure how they join up, and feeling even more anxious than before. This isn't unusual: people often believe things are more complicated than they are, and a measure of stress and anxiety is good for the circulation. Big publishers *are* more complicated than small ones, but only in the way that big machines have more parts in them that can go wrong.

But if it's all so simple, Robyn asks, why did so many publishers back off before one of them took a punt on Harry Potter? Why did publishers turn down Melville and Proust and Hemingway and Orwell and Wells and Nabokov and Joseph Heller and Le Carré and . . . It is deeply mysterious. All editors can have an off day and a blind spot or two, but

54 rejections for David Markson's *Wittgenstein's Mistress*? Those books that win prizes that turn out to have been rejected by multiple publishers? Is serial rejection a calculated initiation rite? A way of culling down to the ones who just won't go away?

All writers have been rejected by a publisher at some point. And it's hard. However sympathetically the rejection is expressed, you can't help but take it personally. Harder than it is for beggars on the street? Robyn asks. Who watch people hurrying by and deliberately not making eye contact?

These used to be, and to an extent still are, the conventions: that during your twenties, or maybe a little later, you get a *proper job* and you *settle down* with a husband or a wife and together you have 2.4 children; and that a novel is a work of fiction of around 256 or 304 pages (a number divisible by 16, for printing reasons); and poetry gets delivered in 64-page books, mostly a poem per page. These conventions worked, for a time: the generations of educated, white, middling-class readers of books in the UK kept coming along at a predictable rate and the reading matter too, both arriving into households that enjoyed a degree of financial security. These are the conventions on which the publishing business is based. (There have always been other kinds of family than the middle-class nuclear one, and other formats in which the words can be delivered, but businesses wanting to stay in business generally have to attend to the 'norms'.) Now, everything is a little more fluid. Definitions of 'proper' jobs and of family and – how surprising – novels too are looser. So when Robyn asks me if I'm working on anything right now I think she is almost expecting me to tell her about something cross-genre, slinky, oddball. I could tell her no, and maybe I *should* tell her no: writers fear that if they talk about work-in-progress, they'll come home to find that all their files have been wiped. But I'm not good at lying. I tell her I'm not yet sure it will come to anything but I'm working on a small book based partly on these chats we're having. Robyn: So it's about me? No, I tell her, she's in there but it's mostly about me. And I have changed her name – that's another convention, 'not her real name'. Robyn asks if there's anything wrong with her real name. Of course not, I say. So keep it, she tells me. And if I want to take a photo of her, go ahead.

A character in Brecht's *Threepenny Novel* advises not to entrust your money to a bank because they'll just use it to pay for their marble-floored buildings in the centre of town. (A character in *War and Peace* says, as I remember it, 'Wherever there is judgement there is always injustice.' Whatever books are for, it's not to deliver little nuggets of wisdom, but certain lines just stick.) Writers can feel this way about the big publishers – who might take their book but lose it among the others, because although they have marketing departments their budgets are mostly spent on the big fish, not the little ones, which are left to flap around and die.

A woman wearing a calf-length red dress walks by *reading a book*. She is royalty; people swerve aside to let her pass. We

turn to watch her down the street. This is the sexiest thing
I have seen all week. Robyn asks: Because she can walk and
read and chew gum all at the same time? Or because what's
on show here is that she has a mind as well as a body? Yes. I
might change my mind if I heard her *speak* her mind, Robyn
says. Or if I knew what she was reading. Business management?
Astrology? They are probably the same thing. We have the
usual discussion about the daftness of the ways in which
bookshops, publishers too, classify their wares. 'Erotica', I
know what that means: this way for pornography, mesdames
et messieurs, *literary* porn, no corner-shop sleaze here. But
every book worth its salt and pepper has an erotic element:
in its moves and its glances, in the shapes of its sentences or
argument, in its confidence or awkwardness. Try reading a few
sentences aloud. Dancing should be on the syllabus of every
creative writing course (but not compulsory).

'The characters in this book are fictional and bear no relation
to actual persons, living or dead.' These disclaimers are there,
I assume, in case of libel actions, but I've always believed they
are part of the fiction.

Robyn felt sold short by the mini-biography of Jack Robinson
on the first page, or maybe the back flap. She wanted some
distinguishing feature – he is bald and ambidextrous, he
collects vintage wooden toys, he makes collages (too obvious:
lots of writers make collage art) – of the kind novelists ascribe
to minor characters in their books. She wanted him to have
been born in Heligoland, just for the sound of it and the

weather; or in a town that used to be in one country and is now in another, so there's ambiguity built in from the start. I recall an author's claim to have worked as a 'dog handler'. It was a nod to the fashion that had authors parading their jobs as dish-washer, trapeze artist, beach lifeguard, scaffolder, priest, actor in porn films, anything that suggested a life beyond just sitting hunched over a keyboard. Not accountant, not estate agent. What exactly *is* a 'dog handler'? I think it was meant to say, keep away. Beware of the dog.

The facts are outrageous. Laundry bills! Parking fines! When I find out that an author has a sister and two older brothers, and they sit in front of a log-burning stove at Christmas playing board games, it throws me. I have to get some air, I have to go for a walk. Most writers' lives are lived *indoors*, but a little light speculation can't hurt. I don't see Jack as a 500-words-a-day writer. More 5,000 some days and other days nothing. I don't think he bothers much with research, I think he just guesses. I imagine that he lives in an apartment on two floors with a spiral staircase and I imagine that he has an assistant who manages his website and books his tickets, in the way that male writers used to have wives who compiled their indexes and sharpened their quills. And a dog. The famous dog. I don't think Jack is troubled by bad reviews, bad dreams, insomnia, jealousy, silicosis (do I mean halitosis?), rickets, woodworm, subsidence. I don't see Jack as humming and hawing about whether or not to buy a hat, then coming back next day and the hat has gone; or as someone who pockets the tip that is meant for the waiter. But he could be.

About Philip Larkin – who claimed to be publicity-shy and refused interviews and who, when he did agree to be interviewed by the *Paris Review*, took five months to answer the first set of questions because he found the whole rigmarole 'insufferably boring' – I have been given more information than I asked for: his lovers, his little-Englishness, his tastes in pornography . . . This barrage of information comes between me and the poems. It has the same effect as a paywall: many potential readers walk away. It didn't used to be thus. Most writers in history never drove a car, let alone had websites and publicists. David Markson in *This Is Not a Novel*: 'Realizing idly that every artist in history – until Writer's own century – rode horseback.' (Keats, for example, 'doing so beside the Tiber each morning until not long before his death'; or George Sand, 'disdaining sidesaddle on a favorite mare she by chance called Colette'.) And most writers knew as they rode their horses that their private lives remained private. I now know far more about many writers than is good for me: their illnesses and playlists, their cats and their children's A-level results, who they vote for and where they go on holiday. I get the full list of ingredients, including things I might be allergic to. I worry that writing has become a public performance of not just virtuosity but virtue, and then I worry *why* I am worrying, if the writing is good. Robyn is reading a new novel and is not enjoying it and when I ask why she tells me that on every page she can hear the author saying, 'Look at me, I'm writing a novel!'

I'm not going to speculate about Jack's or Jennie's sexual history (he says, face straight as a bat, like a politician on being asked if they are going to stand in the next leadership contest). I'll mention instead a biography of a 20th-century poet in which the author stated that the one time the male poet and a named woman slept together was 'not a great success'. So, a medium success? Graded B-minus by both parties? Or was the biographer in the room, hiding in a cupboard and trying to stifle a sneeze? What might 'success' actually mean? Janet Malcolm refers in her book on Chekhov to 'the inescapable triviality of biography'. A mention too of a bookseller friend who was being canvassed by a candidate in an election and she asked him about his party's position on gay rights and he said he was gay himself and she told him that what he personally did with his dick was of no interest to her at all, that was *not the point*.

In some of the photographs of Chekhov he has a full beard, in others no more than light stubble. When Robyn asks me if I have ever grown a beard, I think we are trying to find a way of talking about Chekhov. Chekhov died at the age of 44; almost all of his stories and plays were written when he was half my age.

A ragged urchin, a stalwart sea captain, an elusive writer: certain professions are tied to certain adjectives. Slipperiness does come with the writing territory. The first chapter ('Résumé') of Luc Sante's memoir *The Factory of Facts* begins: 'I was born on May 25, 1954, in Verviers, Belgium, the only child of Lucien Mathieu Amélie Sante and Denise Lambertine Alberte Marie Ghislaine Nandrin.' The family move to America, and then back again, and then forth and back again until 'At length my parents decided to remain in America, at least until the time came when they could retire to Belgium.' In the first sentence of each of the following eight paragraphs Luc Sante is born in the same year in the same place to the same parents, but then the trajectory changes: a move to the Congo, then back to Belgium and the discovery of 'a surprising aptitude for competitive cycling'; or poverty, foster care and arson; or promotion and a villa for Lucien and Denise, for Luc 'a permanent cloud of dope in a waterfront flat' in Goa; or America again, where Luc's father works at a 'a doughnut franchise in Long Island City' and Luc himself is sent back to Belgium; or academic success followed by a career with the Jesuits; or America again, poverty, Lucien arrested as a drugs mule and Luc moving from one foster home to another until he can no longer remember his parents' faces; or to Biarritz, where Lucien's attempt to translate the money raised from selling all their possessions into a fortune at the gambling tables comes unstuck; or decline, decomposition, rats, birds, snow covering the dust and soot covering the snow and 'We grew increasingly warm as we slept.'

Luc Sante's variations are a play on those lines that flash up on the screen to tell what happened to the characters after the film we've just watched has ended: the school joker becomes CEO of a multinational corporation, the champion athlete is stripped of his medals, the bright but shy girl makes a career in private medicine administering pain in prescribed doses to the rich and famous. One life per character – any more would destroy the illusion that these characters are for real.

Another elusive writer: Nina FitzPatrick. She won a literary prize for *Fables of the Irish Intelligentsia*, then the prize was withdrawn because she couldn't prove her Irish ancestry. The paperback edition included a new story, 'The Prize': 'There had been a Stewards' Inquiry. The Winner was not all right.' FitzPatrick's second book, *The Loves of Faustyna*, opens thus: 'In the autumn of 1967 a cloud in the shape of human buttocks appeared over Kraków.' Her not-pen-name name is Nina Witoszek. I tried to track her down and got as far as the Centre for Development and the Environment in Oslo. If she'd made it as far as that, she deserved to elude me.

Staying with a French family in Normandy in the 1960s, I was taken one bright, windy afternoon to see the grave of Jean Cocteau, a local landmark, which turned out when we got there to be the grave of Georges Braque. In her biography of Louise Colet, Francine du Plessix Gray recounts being told of an erotic poem written by Colet in the guestbook of a Vietnamese restaurant on the Left Bank; or perhaps the poem is by Colette, the informant admits; it turns out to be by George Sand, and a forgery. Writers with any degree of fame float free of their work. As a child, I used to think that somewhere out there, maybe in a small town in Chile in the foothills of the Andes, there must be another me, a *spare* me (or I was the spare?); this made more sense than to assume that there was only one me in the whole world.

Harry Mathews: 'I remember a card thumbtacked outside Georges Perec's front door, with "Georges Perec" printed in large lettering, followed by information in smaller print that referred to a housepainter living in another part of Paris.'

Robyn is amused that I haven't read Proust. *Great Expectations?* Yes, but so long ago that what memories I have are probably from a TV adaptation. *Ulysses?* No, but I've seen the film. This confirms Robyn's suspicion that I am not a serious man. It's like going to Paris to see the art and skipping the Louvre, she tells me. There's plenty of other art in Paris, I tell her, in places where the queues are likely to be shorter, but she's not wearing that. Haven't I got a degree in something called Eng Lit? What does that *mean?* Not very much. I spent a lot of time at university avoiding the books I was expected to read; the simplest way was to read other books. All the books I've experienced as formative I've just stumbled across. Essentially I'm an autodidact, with the gaps in my reading history that word implies. And like all autodidacts, I am jealous of the scraps of knowledge I've acquired. There are certain books that mean so much to me I'm reluctant to recommend them to others.

Robyn is thumbing her phone: interiority, stream-of-Instagram consciousness. When she sees me she grins. Someone has sent her a link to an article about the death of the novel, a genre – not the novel but its obsequies – that she had thought was itself deceased, like those articles that claimed the evidence about climate change was a left-wing conspiracy. But it keeps being reinvented, as does the novel, as does the wheel.

118

'The novel in England in this kind of society is passed art. The tradition wanders on in a desultory fashion . . .' That's David Storey half a century ago, one of the writers I was reading for dear life in my twenties and whose own novels are now hardly read. Many of the novel's obsequies are written by novelists.

Perhaps it's not the novel that's dead, Robyn suggests, but us. It's an idea with some distinguished adherents. A number of cherished modernist works are built around the notion that though we may not be clinically dead, we don't know how to communicate with each other or how to act: we don't know *how to live*. There's a lot of mileage in this. Pessoa in *The Book of Disquiet*: 'Living seems to me a metaphysical mistake on the part of matter, an oversight on the part of inaction.' Much of early Eliot is camped in this territory ('A crowd flowed over London Bridge, so many, / I had not thought death had undone so many'). I'm confused: so much political art is conservative in its form and so much 'experimental' art is conservative in its content, playing exquisite music on the lyre while Rome burns.

'I have measured out my life with coffee spoons.' Exactly how many cups of coffee have we drunk, Robyn and I? Some good, some less so, but ordering a coffee buys us time: 'Time for you and time for me, / And time yet for a hundred indecisions . . .' Startling and unsettling when it was first published in 1915, Eliot's *Prufrock* is now a safe set text and you can mug up for your essay from sparknotes.com: the poem 'is an examination of the tortured psyche of the prototypical modern man – over-educated, eloquent, neurotic, and emotionally stilted'. He's had a long innings, this guy; I seem to have been reading about him for much of my life.

Prufrock wondering if he dares to eat a peach is Pessoa worrying about buying a bunch of bananas: 'They might not sell them to me as they should be sold because I do not know how to buy them as they should be bought.'

Rosemary Tonks, 'The Sofas, Fogs, and Cinemas', final lines:

> – All this sitting about in cafés to calm down
> Simply wears me out. And their idea of literature!
> The idiotic cut of the stanzas; the novels, full up, gross.
>
> I have lived it, and I know too much.
> My café nerves are breaking me
> With black, exhausting information.

The first line of 'Poetry' by Marianne Moore: 'I, too, dislike it.' Ben Lerner ('*I, too, dislike it* echoes in my inner ear'): 'The fatal problem with poetry: poems.' After registering their dislike, both Moore and Lerner carried on writing poems. Robyn finds this hilarious: they are characters in a play by Beckett. I tell her about my Polish friend's car, an ancient Volvo which for years he drove back and forth between London and Warsaw. It often broke down, and spare parts were hard get hold of. Eventually it fell to bits. But its sound system was better than that of any car my friend had known, and for listening to music as he drove across Europe, often through the night, that was the car he needed.

Robyn is studying my face intently, as if she thinks she might be asked later – by the police, for example – to describe me. She is looking at me as a child might look, with unashamed curiosity, and I want to tell Robyn, or the child, that writers are not immune to self-loathing. And that writers may well be more prone to self-loathing than others, precisely because their success is measured in worldly terms by the sound of applause, which in order to write well they have to distrust. And that self-promotion through social media, which publishers regularly require of their writers, always leaves an aftertaste of self-loathing.

Hunger for recognition, disdain for commercial success, the perpetual tango of self-belief and self-doubt. And the obsessive quoting of Beckett's 'Fail again. Fail better.' Beckett failed so better that he won the Nobel Prize. You can buy Samuel Beckett fridge magnets.

Another line from Rosemary Tonks: 'my private modern life has gone to waste'. And here's the final line of a poem by James Wright: 'I have wasted my life.' Coming after a languid title – 'Lying in a Hammock at William Duffy's Farm in Pine Island, Minnesota' – and twelve drifting lines of bucolic detail (a butterfly, cowbells, a chicken hawk overhead, the light beginning to darken), that line is a punchline. Secularised, liberated from the seven deadly sins, we still gag at *waste*. Wright's line has been much discussed: a lament? A joke? A boast? Thom Gunn found it 'perhaps exciting' but 'certainly meaningless'. Well-known poet writes much-anthologised poem: few people would consider that Wright has been wasting his life, in a hammock or elsewhere, but allow a writer to mean what he writes. I don't think he felt waste in the morning and probably not the following morning either, but in the late-afternoon moment the poem records in the present tense I think he felt precisely that: 'I have wasted my life.' And then, because it was getting a little chilly, he manoeuvred out of the hammock and wondered what he was going to cook for supper. The feeling surely is, if not an everyday one, not uncommon; there may even be a sort of abandon in surrendering to it; criminals may feel it at the moment they are arrested, or stock-market traders when the figures flash up and they realise they have lost a billion dollars; I wouldn't know. I do know that you can feel it while walking down the Uxbridge Road. (What might be the opposite feeling? 'I have made a success of my life'? That would be Trumpian, not what we expect of our poets, and an even more shocking line.)

My stand-out experience of *I have wasted my life* occurred at sunset one evening in the 1980s at the Taj Mahal in India. The set-up was similar to that in James Wright's poem: idyllic setting, idyllic weather. These are the *conditions* for the feeling that Wright is evoking, which would be very different if experienced when waking in a cold room with a bad hangover. The opening lines of Wright's poem spell out a down-home version of the sublime, before which he cannot help but feel exposed and puny (Mary Wollstonecraft, standing before 'the impetuous dashing of the rebounding torrent' of some waterfall in Norway in 1795: 'I asked myself, why was I chained to life and its misery?'). By the morning after the Taj Mahal, or at any rate within the next few days, I was back on track. My wife still finds this episode funny. It *is* funny, because it's true.

Wasting one's life has pedigree, especially in the male canon. Rilke's 'Archaic Torso of Apollo' ends: 'You must change your life.' Cavafy's 'The City' ends (in Edmund Keeley's translation) with an almost triumphal flourish: 'Now that you've wasted your life here, in this small corner, / you've destroyed it everywhere in the world.' James Wright's line is disturbing not least because it is self-aggrandising: *I have wasted my life.* As if it is a privilege. It is. Compare these lines from Ruth Fainlight's 'The Cripple's Mother':

> Maybe / I have ruined / my life:
> The idea
>   Seems self-indulgent, yet
> Being so vulgar and
> So satisfying,
> It might be true.

No rhetoric; and these are the poem's opening lines, speculation not conclusion, not a cue for applause. 'Maybe . . .' Maybe women and men go about ruining or wasting their lives in different ways; or understanding what waste might mean, or telling about it.

In 1882, the year before he turned forty, Henry James chided himself for 'my wretched habits of work – or of un-work; my levity, my vagueness of mind, my perpetual failure to focus my attention, to absorb myself, to look things in the face, to invent, to produce'. Many of the ideas for stories he rehearses in his notebooks concern missed opportunities, paths not taken, impulses not acted on when the moment was right. In February 1895 he writes: 'What is there in the idea of *Too late* – of some friendship or passion or bond – some affection long desired and waited for, that is formed too late?' He supposes a man and a woman who 'have been dimly conscious, in the past, of the possibility between them' but who have done nothing about this. 'It is a passion that *might* have been' – and the only possible alternative to that passion is 'the wasting of life. And the wasting of life is the implication of death.' He comes back to the idea again in December and in January of the following year. In August 1901 he sketches out what is to become 'The Beast in the Jungle' (published in *The Better Sort*, 1903): a man so convinced that '*something will happen to him*' and so diligently waiting for this ('he doesn't quite know what') that he is blind to the woman who tries to explain him to himself. Only after she dies does he get it: she loved him, and he loved her. 'With his base safety and shrinkage he never knew. *That* was what might have happened, and what *has* happened is that it didn't.'

Given that most people's lives are spent navigating the consequences of neglect, abuse, greed and intolerance, waste may be *the* literary subject. No need to get dystopian about this – waste can be written in terms of personal relationships, as in the Henry James story, and even as comedy (Penelope Fitzgerald: 'for otherwise how can we manage to bear it?'). Hence the abiding literary fascination with the First World War.

I wrote a novel for children aged around twelve, the age of my own children at the time. One of the characters was a Moroccan girl. An agent took me to lunch and suggested I take an Arabic pen name. I mentioned this Robyn, and I also told her that back in the day I published collections of poetry, and it felt like telling her I'd been to Oxford. She has sent me a glossy brochure advertising burial plots in the cemetery for dead white male poets. It looks very pretty but they are running out of space and each time I check online the prices have risen, like for seats on a Ryanair flight.

The agent who liked my Young Adult novel sent me to an editor who said, Yes, but where is this street? And what's in the shops? And what are these people wearing? I sighed. And what's in the pockets of the clothes the people are wearing? And the weather too? Yes, she said, the weather too. I looked out of the window. The ducks were a little excited that day. Cars were doing U-turns. The sky was about to fall in.

Stendhal wanted to be a comic dramatist because he wouldn't have to bother with paragraphs of description: 'I find them so tedious to do, it stops me writing novels.' In his memoirs he drew maps or sketches of rooms and houses and general scenery to save himself the trouble of putting these into words. (And a drawing of a guillotine blade with blood dripping from the slanting edge.) He believed that Walter Scott employed a secretary to go out into the countryside and draft his descriptions of the scenery, and he'd do the same himself if he could afford to employ a secretary. Stendhal didn't even have a ruler; his maps were drawn freehand.

More drawings and diagrams in the books that I read when I was twelve would have been good. We skimmed through books for the 'dirty bits' and when we found them they both excited and disappointed. Just when we really needed books to give us some basic who-does-what-to-who information, they fudged it. They teased. Some of my generation emerged with a sense of resentment towards literature – which had been foisted upon them as a transcendent form of knowledge but told them nothing they urgently wanted to know. Nor were films and paintings much more helpful. In Dai Vaughan's *Totes Meer* an eleven-year-old girl in the 1950s sees some other girls huddled over a magazine; one of them has added pencil marks over a picture of a man in his underpants to make it look as if the pants are stretched, 'with something very big inside them'. On an evening when her parents are out – they have 'gone to the theatre with a business associate of Daddy's and his wife' – the girl opens the glass-fronted bookcase in which her father's art books are kept and riffles through their pages. Raphael, Rembrandt, Van Gogh, Bruegel, Titian: 'nothing, not a single male nude except for the baby Jesus, and I'm not looking for babies'. And then, at last, Michelangelo's *David*: but just 'little snail-curly appendages', and though the girl's heart is beating fast she reckons that this is 'merely the consequence of the furtiveness of my actions'.

I could tell Robyn about something else I am working on but it's so nebulous I have no idea how to describe it. Maybe just the idea of it is enough. Edouard Levé's *Works* describes 533 works 'conceived of but not realised by its author'. In July 1937, in an application for a Guggenheim Fellowship, James Agee wrote, 'I am working on, or am interested to try, or expect to return to, such projects as the following' – and he listed 47 projects. Among them: 'A story about homosexuality and football' ('an inevitable part of it would be a degree of cleansing the air'), 'A new type of sex book' ('as complete as possible a record and analysis of personal experience from early childhood on, and of everything seen heard learned or suspected on the subject'), 'A study in the pathology of "laziness"' ('A story of cumulative horror'), 'Analyses of miscommunication' and 'An "autobiographical novel"'.

Nabokov: 'After reading Gogol one's eyes may become gogolized and one is apt to see bits of his world in the most unexpected places.' Robyn's toasted panini has gone cold. She asks the waiter if he could reheat it. All smiles, all eagerness to please, the waiter leans in close and whispers: 'Just eat it, fucker.' Robyn is delighted. She says it's a line straight out of Jack Robinson and she might use it herself. Then she changes her mind: without the spontaneity, it becomes just a catchphrase. And she'd probably get fired, I add.

Another mistaken assumption I have made: that Robyn's waiting on tables is something she is doing only until she can move on to something she really wants to do (or that pays better, buys more books). She does her job well and she gets good tips. It won't save the world but there are worse jobs. The people she serves are dependent on her, as she is dependent on their paying the bill: a circular power-play. Robyn's father is a retired boat-builder and my father made cast-iron drainpipes and we both tend to romanticise manual labour: at least when you clock off from working with your hands, even if it's only digging a hole, at the end of the day you have sweat on your brow and you can point to *something* – 'There, I dug that grave.' I sit at a desk coining a few sentences that slip by, slip by; Robyn can put smiles on customers' faces; we are both in the services industry. Or the hospitality industry.

Yes, we now have books written by a wider range of writers and made available by a wider range of publishers. But riddle me this, Robyn adds: during the change, hundreds of libraries and bookshops have closed, and to get a starter job in publishing you have to be rich enough to live in London while being paid, if you're lucky, peanuts. Status quo: statistical show of diversity but privilege still in place. In politics, the UK has zero interest in literature other than as a peg for heritage tourism. Anyone appointed arts minister knows it's just a stopgap – see how they get on where they can't cause any harm, and then we might give them a proper job. I tell Robyn that when I started in publishing the places I worked for were unionised, and our employers couldn't have got away with recruiting interns for little or no pay. Robyn looks at me as if she has only just realised how old I am. How's my eyesight? Can I read without glasses? No. Not since a long time. But they're not rose-tinted glasses. I'm not saying things were better then than they are now.

There was the sound of axes being ground. It was loud for two days and then died down. There can be all kinds of reasons for withdrawing your book from a shortlist: she didn't like the way the prize was funded, she didn't want that particular book to 'represent' her, she disliked the judges' choice of the other books on the list – if they rated *that* stuff, then she wanted out. She didn't have to explain. And even if it *was* plagiarism, worse things happen on Mondays.

Plagiarism is a form of kleptomania. Some people steal clothes, others books, others just paragraphs or the occasional line or two. Or an idea, even easier. They slot them into a page of their own writing and if nobody has any objection they do it again. It satisfies a need, even if only for the little thrill of getting away with it. It's an addiction or maybe an illness but not a fatal one, and if the police get onto them they should show some understanding. We all borrow books we forget to give back.

Robyn leans across the table and whispers to me, as if we are in a library. *Silence is requested.* Don't look now, she says, but the man sitting at the table behind you is . . . She names a famous writer. I've read a couple of his books, not the most recent, in fact nothing I can recall in the last ten years, but I *did* read him. I look to see if anyone else – the librarian? – is listening in and then, with the same studious lack of interest with which the librarian is pretending not to overhear us, turn round and take him in, this famous writer. That's *him*? He looks nothing like I remember him, in the author photos. But maybe he never did look like I remember him, except from a certain angle, and with the wind in a certain direction.

Stock figures in male-oriented porn used to include a female librarian: she wore glasses with severe frames, kept a whip under the returns desk and climbed ladders in a short skirt to retrieve rarely requested volumes. Robyn looks at me blankly. The shelf on which 'men's magazines' were displayed in newsagents was itself a high one, not ladder-high but out of the reach of small children. Another blank look from Robyn. *Où sont les neiges d'antan?* Bus conductors? Spam fritters? Verse drama? Standing for the national anthem in cinemas? The recent past – which, as others have pointed out, can feel more remote than the long-ago past – used to coincide with my parents' lives before I was born, and is now the time in my own life before I became a parent.

The near future can feel as remote – as uncanny, as other-worldly: as if the only place for it is in a book – as the recent past. I'm on the pavement next to a construction site, cranes jagging the sky, and I'm looking at the boards around the site which are dressed with a simulation of what will be here in six months: a world without stain, populated exclusively by Generations Y and Z and no one has anything to do except fiddle with their smartphones, drink coffee and shop till they're dead.

Theodora Bosanquet again, on her first meeting with Henry James, who hired her as his transcriber: 'He had, at the best, little hope of any young woman beyond docility. We sat in armchairs on either side of a fireless grate while we observed each other. I suppose he found me harmless and I know that I found him overwhelming.' Joseph Conrad (birth name, Józef Korzeniowski) also hired a female assistant – Lilian Hallowes – to type from his dictation. For a period at the beginning of the last century, Conrad, Henry James, H. G. Wells, Stephen Crane and Ford Madox Ford all lived within a few miles of each other in East Sussex, and after the deaths of James, Conrad and Crane, Ford wrote that they were 'the greatest influence on the literature that has followed after them that has yet been vouchsafed to that literature'. Cynthia Ozick's short novel *Dictation* imagines a meeting between the two transcribers: to retrieve an umbrella, Bosanquet enters a room in which Hallowes is delivering some typed pages to Conrad, in the presence of James. The women exit and walk together – 'under the narrow shelter of the umbrella' – to a Lyons tea shop. They have further outings, and Bosanquet tries to persuade Hallowes to engage in a plot that will guarantee them both a form of surreptitious literary immortality, both in plain sight and invisible: 'two amanuenses, two negligible footnotes overlooked by the most diligent scholarship, unsung by all the future, leaving behind an indelible mark – an everlasting sign that they lived, they felt, they acted!' Hallowes is at first reluctant: what's to stop them being found out? Bosanquet: 'A lack of suspicion, a lack of any expectation of the extraneous. Simply that – and something still more persuasive. The egoism of the artist.' Ozick makes mischief: the story includes Bosanquet's enjoyment of a brief affair with Virginia Woolf, and doesn't shy from the sexual element in the plot she proposes to Hallowes: 'I entreat you: squeeze out the very semen of the thing!' Each man will blindly assume paternity of what the other has fathered. The plot comes to fruition on 'an ordinary Thursday afternoon in the late winter of 1910'. This is a wry nod – it has to be: Cynthia Ozick knows her onions – to Woolf's 1924 essay 'Mr Bennett and Mrs Brown': 'And now I will hazard a second assertion, which is more disputable perhaps, to the effect that on or about December 1910, human character changed. I am not saying that one went out, as one might into a garden, and there saw that a rose had flowered, or that a hen had laid an egg. The change was not sudden and definite like that. But a change there was, nevertheless; and, since one must be arbitrary, let us date it about the year 1910.'

J. M. Coetzee's *Diary of Bad Year* is built around another writer-and-transcriber tangle. An ageing male writer, lusting after a woman in her twenties with 'a derrière so near to perfect as to be angelic' (his words), hires her as 'his tipitista, his clackadackia' (her words) to type out his dictated or handwritten musings 'on what is wrong with today's world'. She's as aware of the set-up as he is: 'he is supposed to be the big writer and I just the little Filipina'; as aware of her status

here as any young waitress in a bar or restaurant in the City
of London; as aware as Coetzee himself is aware of this trope
he's taking on. What does he do with it? Not much. The
woman leaves her boyfriend, moves out of town and sends the
ageing writer fan letters.

Did human character change in 1910? Robyn asks, and for a
moment I think she is assuming that I was on the streets of
London in 1910 myself, dodging the hansom cabs. Perhaps
I was even Mr Smith in Woolf's essay – 'blowing in, so to
speak, on a windy day. He banged, he slammed. His dripping
umbrella made a pool in the hall.' Woolf's is the argument
that every generation needs to have with the previous one.
Respectfully, she takes Bennett, Wells and Galsworthy to the
cleaners: 'to go to these men and ask them to teach you how
to write a novel – how to create characters that are real – is
precisely like going to a bootmaker and asking him to teach
you how to make a watch'. To clear space for herself – to make
that essential room of her own – she needs to distinguish
between *them* (and there's a terrible lot more of *them*) and *us*.
They 'have made tools and established conventions which
do their business. But those tools are not our tools, and that
business is not our business. For us those conventions are
ruin, those tools are death.' A problem for *us* is the present
reading public, 'a very suggestible and docile creature, which,
once you get it to attend, will believe implicitly what it is told
for a certain number of years. If you say to the public with
sufficient conviction: "All women have tails, and all men
humps," it will actually learn to see women with tails and
men with humps, and will think it very revolutionary and

probably improper if you say: "Nonsense. Monkeys have tails and camels humps. But men and women have brains, and they have hearts; they think and they feel" – that will seem to it a bad joke.' The result is 'those sleek, smooth novels, those portentous and ridiculous biographies, that milk and watery criticism, those poems melodiously celebrating the innocence of roses and sheep which pass so plausibly for literature at the present time'. As for what comes next, there will be a smashing and a crashing and a breaking of windows, and for a time everyone will have to 'tolerate the spasmodic, the obscure, the fragmentary', but – an anticlimax, this, after what has come before – 'Your help is invoked in a good cause.' Woolf's essay was written as modernism was getting into gear, but like many classic works it could be restaged in modern dress and feel just as relevant. To answer Robyn's question, at last: no, I don't think human character changed in 1910; and yes, as the essay is written and rewritten, I *am* on the streets of London dodging the cabs, chancing the stop lights.

Robyn: Shouldn't it be '*In* or about December 1910', not 'On'? The oracle has spoken and we query her grammar. 'On' only works if it's a specific day, as in 'On 11 August 1908' – which was a Tuesday and the day on which Lytton Strachey, wandering into a Bloomsbury drawing room and seeing a stain on the dress of Virginia Woolf's sister Vanessa, queried: 'Semen?' This is another date claimed as a hinge between the end of one era and the beginning of another, between the old world of raddled convention and the new world of honesty and openness, though I'm pretty sure than on Wednesday, 12 August, the birds in Fitzroy Square still sang at dawn and an hour later the servants got up to rake out the ashes and start preparing their employers' breakfast.

Conrad's transcriber Lilian Hallowes is a central figure in David Miller's novel *Today*, whose action takes place in the week that Conrad died in August 1924. She is introduced as 'an unhurried, fastidious woman in her mid-fifties who was used to doing what she been told to do', but when the Dean of Canterbury offers her some off-the-peg consolation after the death of her employer she tells him she hates his God and walks away 'in a trance of shy rage'. After the funeral, Conrad's younger son insists that she ask to at least borrow the typewriter at which she has spent her working days, and she reflects: 'For much of her life she had been *called* a typewriter, and now her profession was the name of a sort of machine.' In the first pages of the novel there is – by now there almost has to be – an umbrella. Lilian ('she avoided empty carriages') is in a train compartment with a single other occupant: male, moleskin suit, paisley cravat, round-wire glasses and reading a book, and 'His umbrella's tip now dribbled a shivering pool of water on the compartment's floor.' At Rochester the man exits, and his departure is noted in detail – hat, case from the overhead rack, fumbling in pockets for keys, checking of fob watch – because the important thing is what he does *not* take with him: his book, Forster's *A Passage to India*, published that month in 1924 and which Lilian seizes ('*I am almost a thief*'). 'He left the compartment; he did not look back.' No mention of the aforesaid umbrella. I don't think that every time writers mention the lighting of a cigarette they are bound to record its stubbing out, but they can be as forgetful about umbrellas as anyone else. These often get left behind, stranded in the paragraphs in which they are introduced, while the story moves on.

And hats. 'Pereira maintains that on that occasion he forgot to pay his bill. He got to his feet in a daze, his thoughts elsewhere, and simply walked out, leaving his newspaper on the table along with his hat.' We're in Lisbon again, this time in 1938, in the early pages of Antonio Tabucchi's *Pereira Maintains*. No waiter from the café chases after Dr Pereira with his hat, which is never mentioned again, but later in the day this corpulent, bookish editor of the culture page of a Lisbon newspaper makes his way to another café to meet a much younger student who has engaged something in him that he can't put his finger on: more than curiosity, maybe even a flicker of responsibility. They meet again, and Dr Pereira invites the young student to lunch in a café famous as a meeting place for writers. (Not Pessoa's old haunt, the Café A Brasileira, but another one: a rival gang.) There is a very small number of basic plots.

In another novel set in 1924, *Mothering Sunday* by Graham Swift, the book that the young housemaid Jane Fairchild begins reading on a bewildering Sunday in March is by Joseph Conrad. She has never heard of him before starting to read; by August, when she reads about his death in a newspaper – 'before reflattening it and putting it on Mr Niven's breakfast table' – she has fallen in love with Conrad and determined to become a writer. Sometimes I think that everything is connected, sometimes that this is just a literary illusion.

The dismissal of a housemaid made pregnant by the young master – not uncommon in households employing servants, but Robyn and I are struggling to think of a single novel in which this occurs. Have we forgotten everything we've read? Are books no more than umbrellas, picked up and put down we can't remember where? Meanwhile, according to Wikipedia the number of opium dens in London in the late 19th century has been greatly exaggerated, not least because they feature so strongly in *literature*.

Cynthia Ozick in *Dictation*: 'The forgotten umbrella! Worn device, venerable ruse!' Forster, whose *A Passage to India* was abandoned on a train as casually as an umbrella in David Miller's novel, nailed the use of an umbrella as a device in his earlier *Howards End*. At the end of a concert on a damp autumn evening in London, Helen Schlegel, one of those who rush through life in a dazzle of fine intentions ('I do nothing but steal umbrellas'), takes home an umbrella belonging to Leonard Bast. This simple mistake involving a tatty umbrella – 'It's all gone along the seams. It's an appalling umbrella' – has vast consequences: a long night's tramp through London, unemployment, pregnancy, death beneath a shower of books.

Cynthia Ozick: 'For ten minutes Miss Bosanquet lingered and pondered, lingered and pondered – and there *was*

the question of the umbrella, was there not?' Katherine
Mansfield: 'I can never be perfectly certain whether Helen
was got with child by Leonard Bast or by his fatal forgotten
umbrella. All things considered, I think it must have been
the umbrella.' Pessoa: 'I return home . . . feeling a slight,
confused concern that I may have lost for ever both my
umbrella and the dignity of my soul.' At the start of Graham
Greene's *The End of the Affair*, Maurice Bendrix gets wet on
Clapham Common because he has come out with 'someone
else's umbrella by accident', and it leaks. Vilem Flusser, *The
Shape of Things*: 'We are admittedly surrounded by a lot of
stupid objects, but when it comes to shelter, umbrellas must
be among the most stupid.'

Dr Pereira and the young student arrive together at the café
frequented by writers and Pereira 'looked about him but saw
not a single writer, he maintains. The writers must all be on
holiday, he remarked to break the silence, off at sea perhaps
or in the country, there's no one left in town but us.' Later,
the student leaves Lisbon with a cousin, a printer who knows
how to forge passports, and – but no, it's far too late now
to be introducing a new character. (Actually, why not, just a
chapter or two before a novel ends, have someone walk into
the room and change the whole curve, shift everything onto a
different track?)

'18 January. St Fortunata. This is a lucky day for all people
with umbrellas. They will lose them in the bus.' *Doctor
Partridge's Almanack for 1935* by George Beaton plays merry

hell with pen names: a preface by Beaton ('One of the chief pleasures of writing I find to be impersonation'); an introduction by G. Robinson, Practising Astrologer, to the death and resurrection of Dr Partridge (who died in 1727, was buried under a cellar in Fitzroy Street, and was woken 190 years later by a rat nibbling one of his fingers); a summary by Professor Blush of Partridge's teaching (humanity 'must learn to look forward with a perpetual increase in longing to the great reconciler and deliverer – that is, to death'); a hundred or so prophecies for the year 1935; and, in the copy I'm looking at, a tipped-in slip telling me that the book was 'Presented to the London Library' on 7 November 1934 by 'George Beaton, Esq.' Beaton's one previous book was a novel titled *Jack Robinson*. Beaton was Gerald Brenan, best known for his classic books about Spain. He wrote *Doctor Partridge's Almanack* in two days and nights; in *Personal Record* he described how in writing the prefaces his memories of war and a frustrated love affair 'combined to set up an atmosphere of horror, disgust for life and melancholy that is so far-fetched that it is always on the point of toppling over into absurdity'.

Almost all the signed copies I own are books given to me by their authors. I do have some books signed by their authors for other people: a book of stories by Amy Hempel signed for a couple she met on holiday; a book inscribed by the author with a message of such fulsome gratitude to another writer that I had to rescue it from an Oxfam shop. Strangers asking authors to sign copies of their books is an odd custom. It smacks of touching a hem.

In 1950 *The New Yorker* paid the Canadian writer Mavis Gallant $600 for a story – those were the days – and she packed in her job in Montreal and went to Paris. In a *Granta* interview in 2009 with Jhumpa Lahiri there's this nice exchange: JL: 'Did you ever work in cafés?' MG: 'As a waitress?' JL: 'I meant to write in.' MG: 'No.' And then, MG speaking: 'People worked in cafés when their homes weren't heated. Particularly in the war. That's when you had Simone de Beauvoir and all those people working in cafés, because they had a modicum of heat.' Quintessentially, the activity of writing in cafés is performed in Paris in the decade following a world war (1920s, 1950s), when the clientele comprises artists and hustlers of many different nationalities. The full package also includes a sugar daddy and driving down to Nice on empty country roads with the avenues of trees going *swish-swish-swish* as you speed by with your lover in an open-top car.

Writing in cafés = *working* in cafés? Whatever Robyn and I are saying is interrupted by the noise of a pneumatic drill. We watch in silence as three men in high-vis jackets behind a red-and-white Playmobil fence embed a kind of bollard: spades, buckets, cement, spirit level, brush, pan. It's a fine bollard. Someone writing a book would not disturb us at all, nor would it be so interesting to watch, unless they were working at an ancient typewriter and wearing those green eyeshades worn by journalists in 1940s films. Also from the 1940s is Eliot Elisofon's photograph of Gypsy Rose Lee writing *The G-String Murders* at 7 Middagh Street. It is posed – it's an *ad* for writing, it says writing is sex – but is still my favourite photograph of a writer writing. You're supposed in these photos to be writing *under duress*; Gypsy Rose looks like she's enjoying it. Seated with bare feet in a plush chair, legs splayed, she is working at a typewriter on an adjustable over-bed table; scattered around her on the floor are discarded typewritten pages. Advice for writers: throw away more than you keep; and take off your shoes.

In London in 1970, Murray Bail threw away the manuscript of a book he had written in India, tossing the pages onto the rubbish that was accumulating on the footpath outside his window (the bin men were on strike). 'Yesterday I noticed a woman in an overcoat and trousers standing on one of my pages; remaining near her for a second, tried a sidelong glance to see if it was a good page.'

'These thoughts of mine that you are reading being all that has been salvaged from the scores of sheets of paper now crumpled up in the bin' – from an essay that Italo Calvino spent several years tinkering with in the 1970s before throwing up his hands. What begins as a simple reflection on disposing of the household rubbish turns out to involve sociology and economics (French bin men are 'are a recently immigrated work force obliged to accept the lowliest and heaviest of jobs without proper contracts'), gender politics (the kitchen 'is now seen by women as a place of oppression and by men as a place of remorse'), spirituality ('a rite of purification, the abandoning of the detritus of myself'), physiology (the pleasure he gets from taking out the rubbish 'is analogous to that of defecation, of feeling one's guts unburdening themselves') and 'the long Crisis of the Bourgeois Family'. Calvino signs off with 'a few sparse notes' that he is unable to push through into any conclusive form: 'one is what one does not throw away . . . rubbish as autobiography . . . there is the work that doesn't work, I am no longer there.' But he *is* there, big writer, very present in his choosing to publish his absence. A marker of a writer's success is how interested people are in what's in their rubbish bins.

I suggested an anthology of poems by anonymous and the publisher said I should talk to this other, more famous writer who had made a similar proposal but he was a busy man and maybe he could be persuaded to surrender this book to me. We had lunch. No chance. He told me about the journalists who had been going through the rubbish bins outside his house. Anonymity was a condition he aspired to so no, he was keeping this book for himself.

As much can be gained as lost in translation, but not by me. When I was asked to translate some poems by an Iraqi friend – I was working from literal versions made by the poet's partner, which isn't exactly translation but it's a thing people do – my own versions read like English poems that themselves had been translated into Arabic and then into Dutch and then, why not, into Icelandic and then back into English. My mental horizons were different from those of the poet. In the preface to his translations of poems by Durs Grünbein, Michael Hofmann is instructive: 'I grew up as an English poet: small-scale, occasional, personal, wincingly witty, articulate about dirt.' As a result – 'accordingly, inevitably' – there are poems by Grünbein that Hofmann feels unable even to attempt to translate. Attempts, nevertheless, will be made – 'probably for the first time in history, one's formation as a poet is almost bound to be cosmopolitan nowadays and polyglot, and if it isn't, it damned well should be' – and in the process Hofmann's characterisation of 'an English poet' will itself be changed. It already feels dated.

I like foreign movie posters better than English ones. And advertisements in foreign languages, even better if they have a different alphabet and script, and the labels on jars or cans in the local Polish and Arabic supermarkets – the promise of something just beyond my ken.

Robyn is stopped in the street by a Spanish couple who ask her for directions to the British Museum. Robyn gives detailed instructions: up to the traffic lights, turn left, then straight on for around a hundred yards, then right . . . Much pointing of fingers, much repeating of the instructions by the woman to make sure she has got them right, because she'll be the one who'll cop it if they get lost. Smiles, thank-yous. The man hands Robyn his phone and asks her to take a photograph of himself and his partner; the man smiles, the woman looks down to the ground. Then Robyn and I watch the couple walk up to the traffic lights and turn in the opposite direction to the British Museum. I do that myself, I tell Robyn. They may have changed their minds. They may want to go to the museum *later*. They may have just being trying out a phrase from their guide book.

I used to hitch-hike a lot. It's less common now, either because many people are a little richer or because everyone is more scared of strangers. Both: they fit together. Every trip was a mini-adventure, with risks that applied to both the hitch-hiker and the driver. In Ida Lupino's film *The Hitch-Hiker* two men on a fishing trip pick up a hitch-hiker who has a gun, which is a standard noir scenario, but she gets it: the gun-guy isn't evil, he's just vicious and stupid; the fishing pals in the car are just regular guys and, as the killer tells them, 'soft' – certainly not heroic. They are two against one and could take out the gun-guy at many points but they don't. Safety first. They are relying on the female director to pull them through. She does, in this case, because it's 1953 and Hollywood, but don't count on it.

All writers who have published books that include both fact and fiction know this: readers mistake the fictional for the factual, and vice versa. When these readers discover their mistake, they can feel – as with pen names – that the author is playing games. I'm tired of this, I tell Robyn. Would it help if I printed the book in two colours? Blue for verifiable fact, yellow for the stuff that's made up, green for the overlaps. There'd be a lot of green. Did Marco Polo go to China or not? Does it matter? Does it always have to be binary (fiction, non-fiction)? Binary is not how I go through my days, but people want to believe that something is 'true' – hence those films 'based on a true story'; hence the copy editors who spot inconsistencies and anachronisms and dodgy facts, because any that get through will be jumped on as evidence that the whole project is shaky. But Robyn is not sympathetic today. How can I complain about the lack of trust in experts in public life yet reserve the right to play fast and loose with my own life? Blurring fact and fiction takes me into fake news territory. But I shouldn't over-worry. People generally believe what they want to believe. I could say the Earth is flat and a lot of people would still vote for me. I might get elected.

'Fast and loose'? I'm seeing a man with slicked-back hair in a wine bar in the City of London, a man who can order anything on (or off) the menu he wants and charge it to expenses and no, I don't think so. I hope not.

'He may be at once complete insider and odd man out' – Paul Muldoon, 'Cuthbert and the Otters'.

If you published a book that was neither fish nor fowl (more of a red herring), you would want it placed in a bookshop (if it actually got into a bookshop, which is a big assumption) face-up on the counter by the cash till, wouldn't you? Where else is anyone going to find it? It's not 'Cultural Studies'. It's not 'Essays' (though that will be where they'll bung it). It's not 'True Crime' and not 'History' or 'Smart Thinking' and it's not 'Economics' or 'Gender Studies' (I linger around those shelves, as if I might learn something useful just by standing next to them). You would want it where customers arrive with their clutch of books from the shelves to hand to the bookseller, and look down at what just happens to be on the counter while the bookseller rings up the books and then proffers the card machine for swiping – or if it's over the limit and the card needs inserting, glances out of the window at a seagull passing by while the customer enters their PIN – wouldn't you? You would want the book there on cue when a customer asks if they've got the one about the 2008 financial crash with the same title as a poem by Kipling and a brown cover, and then stands, waiting, *looking down to the counter*, while the bookseller checks on the computer. Robinson, Jack. *Recessional*. 'No, sorry, it appears to be out of print.' *Yes*. An impulse buy. Quick, now, buy this book.

As well as talk, our silences. We're a well-designed page, the text sitting comfortably in the white space around it, the generous margins. Today's weather is breezy and bright with occasional showers. The clouds are being bundled along at a pace. We should really be in the countryside, or at least further out of the centre of town, more sky and more green. I'm imagining a break between sessions at a conference being held at a campus university, the kind with trees and an artificial lake, the conference about pathogens or the Romance languages, and some of the delegates are out on the balcony with coffee and biscuits making small talk, the smokers but not just the smokers, catching up and wondering about this evening's arrangements. There are ducks on the lake. Cut across town, or just a mile away, to a golf course: four men with their bulky bags of clubs are sheltering under a stand of chestnut trees, or another kind of tree entirely, I'm not good at naming trees, calculating whether what's now dripping down is just off the leaves or still rain, and when it'll be safe to resume play. On the fairway a woman is throwing a stick for a dog. The dog chases the stick and runs back and as the woman is tugging to retrieve it, that whole palaver, Robyn butts in: Are there any good golf novels? Baseball and cricket, yes, but golf? There's another silence, during which we both try to think of novels about golf. There's probably something in P. G. Wodehouse but we've both stood shy of that whole strand of reading and we can't think of a single example.

Robyn has given me a bottle of brandy. I'm touched. I'm not fond of brandy but a character in a book I've written is and the bottle will certainly get drunk. After I have thanked her Robyn tells me that she'll be flying to the US next week to see Eric. *Eric?* The boyfriend who gave Robyn a copy of *Recessional* and then went off to New York. What do *I* know? They've probably been phoning or emailing each other in the small hours for months – though Robyn's small hours would not have been his small hours, over there – and that's why she has been complaining of being tired, not because she has been reading all the books on a shortlist. We are book friends, not confessional friends. Except that her mother is dead and her father makes scale models of 19th-century sailing ships, I know almost nothing about Robyn's personal life. I know she has a fear of heights, while I have a fear of caves and underground car parks. I know she lives south of the river, because we have talked about bus routes, and I know she used to smoke and now doesn't, but we have never even asked each other when was the last time a book made us cry. But I like a happy ending and I have offered to drive her to the airport.

Or not phone calls and emails but letters – long, loving, funny, serious, handwritten letters that meander across many pages in sloping lines. Letters that describe the events of their days and the moods of their minds, letters written on trains or in waiting rooms or cafés or late at night at a desk, when the writer is so tired that the effort of going to bed seems impossible and it's easier to stay up, being pulled across a page by a pen. There are (or used to be) people who can write magnificent letters but who become stilted when they attempt to write what we choose to call literature. Think of the time between the sending and the receiving, between the writing and the reading, as an erotic delay.

Robyn goes back to that scene in which the wife is masturbating while her husband is reading a book titled *Slow Mercy*. If Jack or I didn't write it, who did? Updike? Philip Roth? One of the other big male predators? (It actually sounds a little like Jennie. In Jennie's novel a woman who is negotiating a crisis of desire versus duty comes down to her kitchen in the middle of the night to find her husband rearranging their cookery books in complete darkness: 'I want him to tell me what he sees.' There's a fine sentence in David Miller's novel in which Lily Hallowes, going to bed at the end of the day of Conrad's funeral, reaches for the light switch to 'turn the darkness on'.) And if whoever wrote that masturbation scene did go on to write a novel titled *Slow Mercy*, what would that book be about? A serial killer, Robyn suggests.

Surely, Robyn suggests, I can both believe that literature has transformative power and recognise that most examples, not least the ones that claim to have this, simply don't. The latter doesn't invalidate the former. It shouldn't be hard. As long as the presents keep arriving, most children at a certain age have no difficulty in believing that Father Christmas is both a fiction and a fact.

How did Robyn know who I was? (Thank you, copy editor.) During that first brief meeting on a rainy day she didn't ask my name, nor did I tell her. In order to email me – in order to google my name and from there find an email address – Robyn must have read the name on my card during the half-second it took me to present it to the card-reader to pay for my coffee. Is that possible? And if she did google me then she already knew I was also Jack Robinson before I started on my explanation.

Another series of conversations between two people who have read many books features in Chekhov's *Ward 6*. Grumov, a loner, finds comfort in books – 'He used to sit in the club for hours, pulling nervously at his little beard and turning over the pages of periodicals and books' – but develops a persecution complex and ends up in Ward 6, the annexe of the local hospital assigned to mental patients. His books are thrown out by his landlady. Dr Ragin is also a reader: 'He spent half his salary on the purchase of books, and three of the six rooms of his flat were cluttered up with books and old periodicals.' The hospital he presides over is filthy and corrupt and brutal but he does nothing to change this because 'I am nothing by myself, I am only a small part of a necessary social evil'; because we are all going to die anyway so why waste energy on the relief of suffering; and because 'morality and logic' have nothing to do with why he happens to be the doctor and Grumov happens to be the patient, 'It's just mere chance.' But Dr Ragin becomes interested in Grumov, and he takes to calling by Ward 6 for conversation: 'The point is that you and I are thinking individuals.' Grumov, confined, doesn't hold back: 'I want to live, terribly. Terribly!' Grumov calls Ragin out: 'You're a lazy man by nature with a fat flabby body; and for that reason you've tried to organise your life in such a way as to avoid trouble and unnecessary movement . . . We're kept here behind iron bars, tortured, allowed to rot, but all this is wonderful and rational because there's no real difference between this ward and a warm, comfortable study! An expedient philosophy.' Ragin smiles, and tells Grumov that 'the way you've just analysed my character is simply brilliant', and goes home to his books and his beer. People notice them spending time together. Ragin is incarcerated as a patient. He demands to be let out and is smashed in the face by the ward's caretaker. Next day, he has a stroke and dies. Just before his death he sees two things: 'A herd of deer, extraordinarily beautiful and graceful, which he had been reading about on the day before, raced past him; then a peasant woman stretched out a hand to him with a registered letter . . . The postmaster said something. Then everything vanished, and Dr Ragin lost consciousness for ever.' What's remarkable here is that the second last thing Ragin perceives before dying is a flashback not to an actual event in his life but to something he has *read about in a book*;

and then more reading matter is offered him, but it's too late for reading now.

Descriptions in fiction of the subjective experience of dying (and being born) are rare. Chekhov's own death has had a lot of attention: the champagne, the body carried to Moscow in a refrigerated rail wagon for oysters, mourners at the funeral following the wrong coffin. But all of that is peripheral. Dying cannot be *known*; metaphor or allusion is called for. One of the first writers I published, a professional violinist who died aged 37, had a stab at this: 'This is turning out to be the sort of persistent snow that changes plans.' Chekhov's racing deer in *Ward 6* are persuasive to me precisely because they are so greetings-card, so schmaltz, so *bookish*, that I want to say no, no, not that. In a work of fiction, Chekhov nails the unknowability of dying by pointing to the banality of fiction – something of the kind is going on here, and it's an exciting manoeuvre. You could call it metafictional, but there's no need to. On the last page of John Williams's *Stoner*, William Stoner's death is also bookish: his hand seeks out from his bedside table the one book he has published, a book that 'served no use'; there's an 'old excitement that was like terror'; his fingers lose hold, the book slips away 'into the silence of the room'.

Chekhov ends *Uncle Vanya* with a speech that similarly flirts, excruciatingly, with schmaltz. Sonya isn't blind: earlier in the play she has told Vanya that the hay is rotting in the rain and that he drinks too much and lives on fantasy. But on the final page, as she and Vanya resume their thankless work, she attempts to console him: they will work and bear hardship with patience and die, but after death they will be with the angels and all pain and evil will be dissolved in compassion and they will have peace and tenderness and rest. This is her own fantasy. Without being judgemental of Sonya – for lives to be endurable, certain fantasies may be necessary – Chekhov is holding up for inspection the notion that art itself may be consolatory; but books and art do not console, nor is it their business to do so.

When Robert Lowell died in a taxi in New York in 1977, the BBC interrupted the programme I was listening to on my car radio to tell me this. I stopped at the next motorway services and sat for a while in the car park. The deaths of writers who are alive at the same time as me I take personally. How dare they? Coleridge understood this: 'The great works of past ages seem to a young man things of another race . . . But the writings of a contemporary, perhaps not so many years older than himself, surrounded by the same circumstances and disciplined by the same manners, possess a *reality* for him and inspire an actual friendship.' A member of my tribe – next thing I know, they're an ancestor.

When I borrowed books from the mobile library that parked in my village in Yorkshire once a week I assumed the contents page was like the bit of paper inside a box of chocolates telling me which ones had strawberry cream inside them and which had nougat. I turned first to the chapter with the most exciting title; if I liked that one, I would follow it with another chapter chosen again for the promise of its title. If I hadn't read the nougat chapters by the time the mobile library returned, they stayed unread. A friend reads novels in a similar way – opening at a random page, reading for as long as he is interested, then picking up at another page. I sometimes switch on the TV and start watching a film long after it has begun, engaged by images and dialogue before I have any notion of the plot.

Books get left on trains or buses, or they vanish during moves from one place to another. The murder remains forever unsolved, the ambition unrealised, the love unrequited . . . Actually I do know how the love story turned out because I turned to the last page long before I lost the book. In bookshops I often read last pages. I take *browsing* seriously. In life you can't know how it's going to end but in books you can, and I've never seen any reason not to. Robyn asks: But doesn't it kill the suspense? I'm more interested in what's happening now than what's happening next, I tell her, and this sounds glib even as I'm saying it. A more true explanation is that skipping to the end before the author is expecting me there – getting the ending *out of the way* – protects me against anticlimax. Endings so often disappoint.

The writer too can skip, of course. I suspect many novelists write the ending early, then fill in some of the middle bits. The opening pages may be among the last to be written. This is roughly how I used to write essays in exams: start the first one, and then move on to the second or third one, then finish the first one. Robyn looks at me doubtfully. The last time I had to take an exam was so long ago . . . She asks if I used a different quill for each essay.

Endings put a frame around everything that has gone before and we're back to Forster's 'Yes – oh dear yes – the novel tells a story.' Stories are retrospective constructions – *except when I'm reading them*, because even if they are written in the past tense I am reading in the present continuous tense and every single sentence can go any which way. Raskolnikov, with the axe raised, could sneeze; or drop the axe and walk away. He does neither, but then the next sentence too could go anywhere and this (given good writing) is what hooks me. *Will Sam and Chris get back together? Will Heidi get the job, or Miranda? Will Liverpool win the league this year?* The form requires closure; the maintenance of the illusion that books are 'true to life' requires the opposite; many endings end up being tidy and loose at the same time, some of the corners tucked in and others left hanging. There is probably an algorithm for this. It involves a shrug: I'm writing a thing called a novel, you are reading it, let's be sensible about this and meet halfway. Robyn suggests that if I'm anxious about endings I should stop reading about twenty pages before the last one. Or writers could stop writing at around the same stage? But then readers would complain. They have paid their money and they really do want the package wrapped up and tied with a bow. Satisfaction is often followed by a drifting sense of regret.

I've probably left more books unfinished than plates of food.

Stendhal was embarrassed by endings: either he left his books unfinished or he made a dash to the finishing line in a flurry of deaths and exits. There's a price to be paid: in an appendix to his book on Stendhal, Robert Adams lists continuity errors in *The Charterhouse* and *The Red and the Black*, including inconsistences in the ages of characters and their political views and marital status. Adams argues that Stendhal wrote 'in the strict and difficult spirit of the amateur, and the last thing he wishes to have appear on the surface was any mark of the file . . . Fluid, erratic, and defensive, his mind is influenced more by the impulse to achieve or avoid certain effects than by a desire for meaning in depth or systematic consistency.' Ah, says Robyn, the sublime carelessness of the amateur, the affectation that *work* is for dull plodders. What exactly is a 'professional' writer?

A joke without its punchline is not a joke. Except when it's told by a child who hasn't yet understood the genre's basic requirement. A book of meandering jokes without punchlines – shaggy dog stories, really – is something I'd like to write. Occasionally, just a punchline, forget the foreplay.

Explaining a joke to someone who hasn't got the joke is tiresome. They resent me for making them feel stupid for not having laughed; I resent them for making me drain all the humour from the joke by spelling it out. We are not feeling best disposed. Oh, I get it now, they say, and may even smile, but now is too late.

I walk fast, Robyn tells me, wheeling her bike beside me as we head towards the café for her early evening shift. Am I running late? I don't think so. But lateness *is* an issue. I have frantic, sweaty dreams about being late. I think of myself as a late developer, and I have a lot of *catching up* to do. That at school I was beaten for being late is also probably relevant: the relationship between distance and time is always tinged with anxiety. Those people who stroll nonchalantly onto the platform one minute before the train departs are surely wizards: they can pause the clocks. The anxiety gets into the practice of writing: when I have started writing something I'm impatient for it to *have been written*. I'm not worried about someone else's take on what I'm writing being *better*, simply that I'll be late. Robyn has noticed this: it is part of my not attending properly to what I am doing. Then she checks her watch and gets on her bike – she has just five minutes to get to the café before her shift starts. I watch her veer into the middle of the road to overtake a bus and almost get smashed by an oncoming van.

I'm winding up my watch, because I forgot to do this last night and it stopped while I was asleep. Robyn asks: Do we want to talk about eBooks? Probably not. It's curiously satisfying, winding up my watch; like winding up a clockwork toy, or sharpening a pencil. My mother let me wind up the grandfather clock in the hall, with a great big key. I stood on a wooden stool to do this. When driving a car, to signal that you were about to turn left you stuck your arm out of the window and made a kind of circular motion, again like winding something up. Turning the pages of a book is winding the narrative on. I'm not, yet, a full-on Luddite – I have electricity, and a washing machine – but I worry that I'm bargaining away my agency for ease and convenience. *Ease* makes me uneasy. Exactly how much agency am I prepared to surrender for exactly how much ease? Robyn remarks: I'm a bit late to the game, maybe? The negotiations are over. They never really took place. People feared for their safety when moving stairs were first introduced, now everyone's on the escalator. In many lifts – Robyn read this in *The New Yorker*, so it must be true – the 'close-door' button isn't connected to anything, it's just there to give people the illusion of agency.

Honeymoon period: the time between finished copies of a book becoming available and its publication date, when it rubs up against the world's indifference. It's too late now for the editor to change their mind or for the publisher to go bankrupt, and even if the warehouse with the printed copies inside it burns down at least I have *my* copies, and during this brief window I can still believe that the book might change things. It will vanish like the rubbish bags on the day the bin men come, gone before I have even made coffee.

Robyn, while the tables around us are being cleared: We *will* go on reading, won't we? Pause, in which each of us contemplates a world in which the physical space occupied by books is grown over by weeds. She's asking me to put my arm around her shoulders and – while libraries close and sea levels rise and we head up shit creek without a paddle – tell her that it will be OK. She's asking me to tell her that she can go to sleep safely and not have bad dreams and when she wakes up in the morning Mum and Dad will still be there and the dog too and the sun will be shining. I could tell her yes, there will still be books and there will still be coffee too, and if there isn't coffee we won't have to worry about cockroaches falling into our cups in the morning, there will certainly be cockroaches, but it's not my job to say this and she knows it. The question she's really asking, I think, is will there still be kindness and intelligence? Yes, but I can't promise. Both Robyn and I consider books to be essential to our lives, and believe we would not be the people we are without them, but compared to food and shelter and love they are add-ons. If we don't know this we don't deserve more books. But I do promise Robyn that I'll stop going on about Stendhal, he's not exactly a role model. It's not much of a promise, I know.

Also, Robyn pleads, no more umbrellas. We've had enough umbrellas. Most of the fictional umbrellas I have mentioned here have been Edwardian, or at least from the early 20th century. Umbrellas in England go with bowler hats and starched collars and cufflinks and moustaches and upholstered train compartments and porters and gaslight and male entitlement. Every time I mention them, Robyn says, she has a kind of *damp* feeling.

Edwardian umbrellas were substantial items. If your umbrella broke, you paid someone to repair it. Umbrellas were essentially male accessories and urban (in the countryside you wore a cape); and being urban, they were also accessories to modernism. T. S. Eliot collected them. In 1950 Irving Penn took a studio photograph of Eliot: tie, overcoat, sleeked-down hair with parting, shoes polished that morning, in his right hand a briefcase and in his rigidly outstretched left hand both a hat and a tightly furled umbrella whose handle is larger than Eliot's own hand. It's a third leg. It's a ceremonial weapon. How stiff can you get, without being actually dead? The photograph is a portrait of a tribal elder in traditional costume (and is of the same ilk as Penn's ethnographic photographs taken in Morocco and New Guinea). It's a portrait of 'an autocratic, inhibited, depressed, rather narrow-minded and considerably bigoted fake Englishman' (Cynthia Ozick, in an essay in which she recalls growing up in an era in which Eliot 'seemed pure zenith, a colossus').

From a taxi in Paris Evelyn Waugh saw a man whose umbrella was on fire. A friend was once dowsed with water by a stranger in the street because, smoking and careless, he had managed to set fire to his tote bag, which contained a copy of the *TLS*.

Fewer umbrellas, more rain . . . Swimming in the rain. Singing in the rain. Crying in the rain. Crying in the rain while riding a bike, Robyn adds, and sloshing through puddles. Reading in the rain: probably not. All the lovely

poems about rain. 'Westron wynde, when wyll thow blow /
The smalle rayne downe can rayne?'

Lisbon again, and another confusion of identities. In 1940
Lisbon was crowded with refugees from all over Central
Europe seeking a passage across the Atlantic to escape from
the Nazis. Sixty years later, the narrator of Cozarinsky's
'Hotel Emigré', following research in New York, travels to
Lisbon to discover more about his American grandmother
and the two German refugees she had met while serving
with the International Brigades in the Spanish Civil War.
Theo is Jewish, Franz is not. She tells them that she cannot
facilitate immigration visas by marrying both of them because
the US authorities won't permit any fancy arithmetic, but
that institutions are mobilising to save Jews from danger.
In Lisbon in September 1940 she marries Theo in Lisbon
and embarks with him on the *Nea Hellas* for New York.
(The ship's other passengers include a son and a brother of
Thomas Mann.) Franz is left behind. In 2000 the narrator
begins to suspect – 'believe? hope?' – that the man entering
the US with Theo's passport, and who was to become his
grandfather, was in fact Franz. The penultimate scene of
'Hotel Emigré' takes place in a bookshop in Sintra whose
aged proprietor, who knew many of the exiles adrift in Lisbon
in 1940, recognises the narrator as 'a member of the ancient
tribe of book people – not a bibliophile anxious to get his
hands on rare first editions, but simply someone for whom
words printed and kept between two covers are worth any
amount of living and worldliness'.

The narrator of Cozarinsky's 'Hotel Emigré' cannot establish the true identity of his grandfather by direct questioning, however tactful, because by the time he travels to Lisbon in 2000 his maternal grandparents have both been killed in a car accident. Random deaths are hard to make sense of because there is no sense to be made: just a few seconds earlier or later and . . . Deaths from road accidents – and from street stabbings and falling off ladders: let road accidents stand here for all such – violate our sense of what is supposed to happen next. Most deaths in fiction are *plotted*, timed to the exact page or paragraph and given meaning by what comes before and after, and in life we expect the same. But – Cozarinsky again, in *The Moldavian Pimp* – 'reality has a tendency to ignore the need for verisimilitude we demand of fiction'.

'And they lived happily ever after': the old formula wasn't just a handy cliché, a socially acceptable way of marking a departure: goodbye, goodbye, drive carefully. It worked as a sophisticated trope and a convenient collusion. It acknowledged the fictiveness of the story – no one intelligent can believe that anyone's life will be an unending bed of roses, however much they are in love – without requiring either storyteller or reader to openly admit this.

Nabokov in *Pnin*: 'Some people – and I am one of them – hate happy ends. We feel cheated. Harm is the norm. Doom should not jam.' Nabokov's 'we' is far from everyone. Gianni Celati has a story about a chemist whose life has been hard –

his pharmacy is destroyed by the Fascist brothers of a girl he loves – and who in his last years 'devoted himself to rewriting the endings of some hundred or so books in every conceivable language. By inserting small strips of paper over the passages that had to be rewritten, he changed the outcome of the stories, bringing them unfailingly to a happy ending.' In the days before his death he tackles *Madame Bovary*: 'In the new version, Emma recovers and is reunited with her husband.' Recovers from arsenic poisoning or from dissatisfaction with her marriage? I think he means both.

Emma Bovary didn't *have* to kill herself. Nabokov neglected to mention that miserable and doomy endings can be as much a convention – and a form of cheating – as happy ones. Crime novelists have played this often: pages of sex and violence but in the final chapter the guy or the girl gets strapped into the execution chair, so it's a *moral* book. Statistically, in life not literature, most (in no particular order) murderers, thieves, rapists, child abusers and corrupt politicians get away scot free. The ones I read about who get caught are the exceptions. Doom does jam, and deposed dictators live out their lives beside swimming pools in luxury exile.

Have we covered everything? We have barely begun. Alcohol, Amazon, American English and British English (and the latter's prissy insistence on every teensy preposition), audiobooks, blurbs (and puff quotes from other authors on covers), dedications, fonts, footnotes and endnotes, illustrated books, lost books, remaindered books, books pulped because of libel actions, books banned by popes and others who know better than the rest of us, lost manuscripts (T. E. Lawrence, Malcolm Lowry), first books and last books, first lines and last lines, books which have made me cry, 'comic' books that never even raised a smile, books which even at the third attempt I gave up on, books which I have wanted to never finish, split infinitives and other grammar obsessions, books bought because of the promise of a single poem or paragraph and that fail to live up to that promise, novels that include characters who are writers (and samples of their work, which of course might also include characters who are writers), masterpieces of world literature which I will never read, books written collaboratively by two or more authors, books in waiting rooms and books left behind by previous guests in the lobbies of small hotels in foreign towns, books I know I've got but cannot find (so buy another copy), books that are so ineradicably associated with certain people or places or episodes in my life they have lost all autonomy, reading books in the back seat of a car (in childhood, this made me carsick), reading under the bedclothes after lights out (can reading make you go blind?), reading in the bath (damp books, swollen pages), reading on the beach (sand between the pages), reading while eating (smears of ketchup or gravy), reading aloud for long after the person I am reading to has fallen asleep, book clubs and reading groups, public libraries and private libraries (such as the one that has bats in it, to eat the worms), why titles on the spines of English books read from the top downwards while on (most) French books they read from the bottom upwards (and so when a book is lying flat, its cover facing up, you have to be upside down to read the title on the spine), famous writers' famous dogs (and Flaubert's parrot and Gérard de Nerval's lobster), storage and shelving issues, periodic dispersal of books to charity shops, the number of people attending a poetry reading that officially constitutes 'a lot', the correct pronunciation of Gogol and of Nabokov (who wrote in his book on Gogol: 'One cannot hope to understand an author if one cannot even pronounce his name'), attempts to render dialect or other non-standard English on the page, direct speech rendered without the fuss of quote marks, attempts to bribe reviewers (cash, sex, drugs, status: the usual currencies), tote bags, entry fees for literary prizes, literary jokes, literary lunches, recipes in novels, favourite deaths of authors (Thomas Urquhart, said to have died during a fit of laughter on learning that Charles II had been restored to the throne), favourite deaths of characters in novels (Hugh Person's father in Nabokov's *Transparent Things*, who dies while trying on a pair of trousers), misprints and typos and other such errors ('Thou shalt commit adultery': the printer of that edition of the Bible was fined £300 and spent the rest of his life in a debtors' prison), the *weight* of books (James Salter: 'Nothing is heavier than paper'), unreliable narrators, unreliable authors (at the end of Maupassant's story 'Rose' I'm pretty sure he's got the sequence of speakers out of sync, and none of the translators has called him out on this), unreliable *readers*, hatchet-job reviews ('*Intimacy* is a short, odious and if you like yellow, attractive-looking book'), film and TV adaptations, sequels (and prequels), ghost writers (and ghost readers), writers who disappeared (Weldon Kees, Antoine de Saint-Exupéry, Ambrose Bierce, B. Traven, Rosemary Tonks), writers' superstitions, writers' illnesses (syphilis, tuberculosis, haemorrhoids; hypochondria, *passim*), the use and abuse of the semicolon (Murray Bail: 'Living in England I find I am using the semicolon more, as if all statements here are qualified'), why literary folk tend to lean left (but usually not far left, they don't want to fall over) rather than right, chick lit and bloke lit, 'minor' writers and minor characters . . .

No, I don't miss the pre-word-processing, pre-internet days of carbon paper and Tippex, when every poem I sent to a magazine had to be typed from scratch and posted off with a stamped and self-addressed envelope enclosed for its return. I do miss the smell of bonfires on chilly autumn afternoons.

The lack of electronic files made distributing work laborious, but destroying it was much easier. Incineration was the preferred method. The burnt pages include Byron's unpublished memoirs, Sylvia Plath's diary of her last months, Emily Hale's letters to Eliot and sheaves of letters to (or from) Dickens, Henry James and Flaubert. Ash, rising and settling. Flaubert was as conscientious in destroying text as he was in creating it: the fire that he started after supper with Maupassant on a May evening in 1879 lasted for eight hours, continuing through to dawn.

Among the letters fed to the flames by Flaubert – it's assumed by the scholars who have looked for them – were those sent to him by Juliet Herbert, an Englishwoman who in around 1855 was employed as a governess for his niece Caroline and who soon afterwards began giving English lessons to Flaubert himself. They worked together on an English translation of *Madame Bovary*. After Herbert returned to England, bringing with her the translation of *Bovary* to seek out a publisher, Flaubert made three visits to London to see her, and in the 1870s she visited Flaubert in Paris several times. Flaubert died in 1880; Juliet Herbert died in 1909 in Shepherds Bush, west London, five minutes' walk from where I am writing this. Flaubert's letters to Juliet Herbert are lost, presumed destroyed; also that first translation of *Madame Bovary*. (The first published translation was by Eleanor Aveling, a daughter of Karl Marx.) Whenever I pass a local house that's being renovated, I pause to watch what's being hauled out of the attic and dumped in a skip.

Stendhal: 'In 1821 I had great difficulty in resisting the temptation to blow my brains out. I drew a pistol in the margin of a bad play about love I was scribbling then . . . It seems to me it was political curiosity that stopped me doing away with myself; perhaps also, without suspecting it, I was frightened of the pain involved.' That's a pose, surely: if you don't want to die before knowing how an election pans out, or if Robyn really will get back together with her ex, then you don't want to die. 'Aubade' by Philip Larkin – who liked cricket and would have been unhappy to die in the middle of a Test match – is much obsessed with 'the total emptiness for ever, / The sure extinction that we travel to'; the poem ends with the line 'Postmen like doctors go from house to house', and I think of the woman who delivered a registered letter to Dr Ragin in the moments before he died, a letter whose contents we will never know (though they are unlikely to have included the 500 roubles Dr Ragin had lent the postmaster to pay off his gambling debts). Meanwhile, the friend I used to visit in a care home and read aloud to has died; I was annoyed with her for dying before we had finished reading a book we were both enjoying, but on reflection we stopped at exactly the right place, halfway through the book at a moment of complete happiness.

Robyn tells me that she had no idea, on the day when she ran after me with the book I'd left in the café and I gave her my email address, that we'd be seeing so much of each other. Me neither. But I have no memory of giving her my email. She tells me I wrote it on the back of the envelope I was using as a bookmark, and because I didn't have a pen I had to borrow hers. We look at each other coolly. She is thinking I'm getting to the age where I can remember what I was wearing on a Saturday afternoon sixty years ago but not what I had for lunch today, or even if I've had lunch. Or, less generously, that I'm a writer of fiction who chooses what to put in and what to leave out, what to remember and what to forget. I ask her if she thought at the time that I was the kind of man who presses his contact details on waitresses and she says yes, of course it had crossed her mind.

Art galleries are exhausting; libraries have more chairs, but even in libraries I can't smoke. I used to twiddle with my hair and then I took up smoking. I get pleasure from the nicotine but doubtless also from having something to do with my hands, and putting something in my mouth. Fidgeting is often considered a sign of impatience, or boredom. Those are different things. Boredom is not waiting for something to start, or end, but an abstraction from all that; it can be an incubator for invention as well as random mischief.

When one of us wins the lottery, Robyn and I will open a café of our own. Music yes, TV no. On Tuesday evenings, a table reserved for members of the local hagiographical society, who are both enthusiastic and disputatious, so the bar tab will keep mounting. A yard out the back for smokers, and an ancient propeller ceiling fan with lazy blades that slow everything down. Somewhere to hang your hat and stand your umbrella, and those long poles on hinges for newspapers. Robyn shakes her head – not the poles. A dog or a mynah bird? Poetry readings? Again Robyn looks at me doubtfully. We don't want to try too hard, she says. Let's not over-design.

If I did give Robyn my email address on that rainy day at the start of all this it was because I was ridiculously surprised to meet someone who had read something I'd written. For writers whose readership doesn't extend far beyond family and friends, this is rare.

The waiter was very old. After he'd taken our order, his hand shaking and his head bent so close to the notepad he was almost rubbing it with his nose, the four of us around the table fell silent. When we started speaking again, we realised that each of us had been wondering whether he'd live long enough to bring our food to the table.

Surfacing, coming up for air – when my eyes move off the printed page and take in the world around me: traffic, voices, a shopping mall passing by as the train gathers speed, a dog saluting a litter bin. There is a moment at the kitchen table when, pausing in my reading of a magazine piece, I think that the voices on the radio are talking about the same subject (they are not); a moment, waking from a dream, when the dream and the so-called real world are entangled; a moment, coming indoors from a sunlit garden, when my eyes are confused. I am an emissary from one dominion to another, and back again, and back again, stuttering when asked to deliver my message. The border is a permeable membrane, invisible but *felt*: a cloud passing over the sun. Crossing back and forth can happen at any time during the reading of a book but the moment is most affecting (because it involves loss) when I raise my eyes from the page on which used to be printed in small capitals, THE END: Emma has died in agony after swallowing arsenic; Charles, with a lock of Emma's hair in his hand, has also died, while his daughter thought he was 'only playing'; the pharmacist Homais has received the Legion of Honour.

Any justice delivered by *Madame Bovary* is not in the death of Emma, which was abetted by the requirement that authors and publishers and printers uphold the moral codes signed off by church and state, but in the counterpoint of that with the ludicrous Monsieur Homais getting the medal he has coveted. And in the telling rather than the tale: *there's* the rub. Awkwardness is a given, clumsiness even, because the job is so hard; sometimes the justice is in the awkwardness.

John Halifax, Gentleman by Dinah Craik resided in the glass-fronted bookcase in the house in Yorkshire in which I grew up, its title horizontal on its green spine. I assumed the book was about a man from Halifax, but I'd never been to Halifax so I didn't read it and still haven't, either been to Halifax or read the book. In fact the book is about, according to the plot summary on Wikipedia, a poor orphan in Gloucestershire who, 'through honest hard work', eventually 'achieves success in business and love, and becomes a wealthy man'. Ah, one of *those* books – the kind that well-meaning uncles gave to their nephews and nieces and that that foist upon their readers a bargain-basement, one-size-fits-all, imitation justice.

Clocks were standardised in the UK when the railways arrived and timetables were needed, which is analogous with attempts to standardise punctuation following the invention of printing, and I start to tell Robyn about my father boarding a train for Glasgow and getting off in Sheffield but immediately begin to worry that I've told her this before and Robyn is just being polite in not pointing this out, or maybe the first time round she switched off but she's prepared to give it another listen, just in case where I get to is worth the preamble. Are we running out of things to say, or ways to talk about them? It's more likely that at this stage repetition is part of how it works. It's a form of reinforcement. There are stories that children want to hear again and again, there are books I want to reread.

The ending is in sight. The polls are closed, the summing-up speeches are over. But we're not quite there yet. While the votes are being counted, each candidate prepares two speeches: one expressing humility in victory, the other demonstrating magnanimity in defeat. While the jury is deliberating behind locked doors, the journalists are preparing two front pages: innocent of all charges, guilty as hell.

West Yorkshire, summer 1968. I am seventeen years old and I'm working on a small hill farm with rocky fields and 55 cattle. I spend many hours chasing cows that have escaped from the fields onto the narrow roads, cajoling them back (they are bigger than me) and then mending the fences with bits of string. In September I'll be returning to school to take the entrance exams for Cambridge, and at Christmas the period of my life that has been school will be over. That the farmer has a limp is, I feel, important but I do not know why. He has never before had a hired man, he can't afford one – he can't even afford me, a skinny anorexic who's happy with whatever little cash is in the grubby brown envelope that's silently pushed across the kitchen table on Friday evenings, but for some reason I am here and his wife, seizing her chance, goes with their small child to her mother for a holiday, the only one she has had in a decade. During the past week the mist has clung to the ground until late in the morning; the farmer and I have lazed over lavish fry-up breakfasts, delaying the milking, because he's on a kind of holiday too, while the cows mooed their impatience, and for perhaps the third or fourth time in my life I have thought, take away work and routine and bits of string, and how quickly the wilderness moves in. It's not an abstract thought, this week. Today, a sunny Saturday afternoon, after milking the cows I'm walking a couple of miles home to see my mother, and on the way I lie down at the edge of a wood to read my book, a Signet paperback edition of *Anna Karenina*. I smell of cattle; later, at home, I'll have a bath. Meanwhile, Anna and Vronsky in Moscow, sunlight through leafy branches in a dormitory suburb of Leeds – that membrane again, barely a comma. And the other one, between now and then.

Would I have 'got more out of it' if I'd waited to read *Anna Karenina* until I was older? A capitalist reckoning of what literature is for: profit. The notion that grown-ups should be seen and not read, at any age, is ridiculous.

When she goes there'll be a hole in my life the size and shape of a particular person sitting opposite me at a café table. In time, perhaps, the hole will be filled by another particular person, probably of the female kind – because ever since I was reading tales of empire and derring-do in a leather armchair in the library of an all-boys school the lessons that I've learnt have been taught by women. It hasn't been easy for them: one of my end-of-term reports from that school reads (1962),

'Trying hard but finds the work difficult'; another (1963), 'No flair, but he plods on.' I've needed to unlearn things I thought I knew and then to listen to very basic explanations, often again and again. I've wondered what's in it for the women. But ignorance serves no one well.

Dream. Stendhal is arriving in Namibia. He is framed in the doorway of an Air France plane, at the top of the disembarkation steps. He is wearing a bright blue frock coat. Apart from a couple of single-storey airport buildings, the rest is desert.

There is no photograph of me sitting in the chair next to Pessoa outside the Café A Brasileira in Lisbon because I never actually sat in that chair. On the day in the summer of 2019 when I'd planned to go there I got distracted by a flea market in the Alfama district. The sun was hot, the market was busy – people like poking around, hoping to find something for nothing but not really minding if they don't. A man was selling old photos out of a battered suitcase: sunsets, parties, babies, men in uniform and a middle-aged woman standing on a bridge over a motorway. She looked Austrian, or maybe Dutch. A handsome woman, a little overweight, a little chubby. There she was again, on a street corner, still smiling for the person who loved her, or who loved taking photographs of her. Shuffled among the hundreds of other photos, she kept recurring, always alone and always holding her handbag in front of her with both hands and always in bland, anonymous locations: a supermarket car park, a dusty back yard, a garage forecourt, a field with thistles. I briefly wondered about the contents of her handbag and what work she did but she was probably retired by now, and she and her photographer companion did a lot of travelling.

We get to the airport early and have coffee in the departures hall before Robyn checks in. Her luggage is heavy but I don't ask what books she has packed. She crosses her left leg over her right and I see that her foot is trembling: a nervous tic or something we should be talking about, something I should have picked up on long before now? But again I don't ask. For all that it was Robyn who initiated this to-and-fro, first chasing me in the street and then emailing me, she is basically shy, and so am I, like a lot of people for whom books are important. We are talking about novels of New York and the conversation is a little *desultory*, as if we know we are winding down and there's no point in setting a new hare running now, and we are about to say goodbye when we are interrupted by a public announcement: 'Would the passenger travelling under the name of Jack Robinson booked on flight BA7008 to Doha please come to the information desk.' *Doha?* Robyn and I look around the hall. A safe bet is that no one else here even knows who Jack Robinson is. Each of us is going to a different place, each with our bits and pieces, and we can't help but notice the number of guns around – terror and security, both. A man with a limp is wheeling his luggage towards the information desk. 'It must be your agent,' Robyn says. I don't have an agent.

REFERENCES

Adams, Robert M., *Stendhal: Notes on a Novelist* (Merlin Press, 1959)

Agee, James, *The Collected Short Prose*, ed. Robert Fitzgerald (Calder & Boyars, 1972)

Amichai, Yehuda, 'Nina of Ashkelon', in *Penguin Modern Stories 7* (Penguin, 1971)

Bail, Murray, *Notebooks 1970–2003* (Harvill Press, 2005)

Barthes, Roland, 'The Writer on Holiday', in *Mythologies*, trans. Annette Lavers (Paladin, 1973)

Beckett, Samuel, *Mercier and Camier* (1970; Faber, 2010)

Berger, John, 'Giorgio Morandi', in *The Shape of a Pocket* (Bloomsbury, 2002)

Birdwell, Cleo, *Amazons* (Henry Holt, 1980)

Bosanquet, Theodora, 'Henry James': https://fortnightlyreview. co.uk/2018/06/mr-james-miss-bosanquet-and-her-palpitations

Buchan, James, *Slide* (Minerva, 1992)

Calvino, Italo, 'La Poubelle Agréée', in *The Road to San Giovanni*, trans. Tim Parks (Vintage, 2009)

Celati, Gianni, 'A Scholar's Idea of Happy Endings', in *Voices from the Plains*, trans. Robert Lumley (Serpent's Tail, 1989)

Chekhov, Anton, 'Ward 6', in *Lady with Lapdog and Other Stories*, trans. David Magarshack (Penguin Classics, 1964)

— *Notebook of Anton Chekhov*, trans. S. S. Kotelliansky and Leonard Woolf (Ecco Press, 1987)

Coetzee, J. M., *Diary of a Bad Year* (Vintage, 2008)

Cozarinsky, Edgardo, 'The Sentimental Journey', in *Urban Voodoo*, trans. Ronald Christ and the author (Lumen Books, 1990)

— 'Emigré Hotel', in *The Bride from Odessa*, trans. Nick Caistor (Harvill Press, 2004)

— *The Moldavian Pimp*, trans. Nick Caistor (Vintage, 2007)

Defoe, Daniel, 'A Narrative of all the Robberies, Escapes, &c. of John Sheppard', in *Defoe on Sheppard and Wild*, ed. Richard Holmes (Harper Perennial, 2004)

Dillard, Annie, *The Writing Life* (Harper & Row, 1989)

Dyer, Geoff, *Out of Sheer Rage: In the Shadow of D. H. Lawrence* (Little, Brown, 1987)

Enright, D. J., *Collected Poems* (OUP, 1981)

Fainlight, Ruth, *Poems: Ruth Fainlight, Ted Hughes, Alan Sillitoe* (Rainbow Press, 1971)

Fitzgerald, Penelope, 'Curriculum Vitae', in *A House of Air: Selected Writings* (Flamingo, 2003)

FitzPatrick, Nina, *Fables of the Irish Intelligentsia* (Minerva, 1992)

— *The Loves of Faustyna* (Fourth Estate, 1994)

Flaubert, Gustave, *Madame Bovary*, trans. Geoffrey Wall (Penguin Classics, 1992)

Ford, Ford Madox, *The Good Soldier* (1915; Penguin, 1976)

— *The Bodley Head Ford Madox Ford*, Vol. V: *Memories and Impressions*, ed. Michael Killigrew (Bodley Head, 1971)

Forster, E. M., *Howards End* (1910; Penguin Classics, 2000)

Gallant, Mavis, 'The Ice Wagon Going Down the Street', in *Paris Stories*, ed. Michael Ondaatje (NYRB, 2002)

Halfon, Eduardo, *The Polish Boxer*, trans. Ollie Brock, Lisa Dillman, Thomas Bunstead, Anne McLean and Daniel Hahn (Pushkin Press, 2012)

— *Mourning*, trans. Lisa Dillman and Daniel Hahn (Bellevue Press, 2018)

Hare, David, *Wetherby* (Faber, 1985)

Hayes, Alfred, *In Love* (1954; Penguin, 1961)

— *The End of Me* (Atheneum, 1968)

Hofmann, Gert, *Lichtenberg and the Little Flower Girl*, trans. Michael Hofmann (CB editions, 2008)

Hofmann, Michael, interview with Fran Brearton, *Thumbscrew*, Spring/Summer 1999

— Preface to Durs Grünbein, *Ashes for Breakfast*, trans. Michael Hofmann (Faber, 2006)

Hrabal, Bohumil, *Too Loud a Solitude*, trans. Michael Henry Heim (Abacus, 1993)

'Ivar's Story', in *Hrafnkel's Saga and Other Stories*, trans. Hermann Pálsson (Penguin Classics, 1971)

James, Henry, *The Complete Notebooks of Henry James*, ed. Leon Edel and
   Lyall H. Powers (OUP, 1987)

Jarman, Derek, *Kicking the Pricks* (Vintage, 1996)

Kafka, Franz, *Amerika*, trans. Michael Hofmann (Penguin, 2007)

Kertész, André, *On Reading* (Penguin, 1982)

Lerner, Ben, *The Hatred of Poetry* (Fitzcarraldo Editions, 2016)

Lethem, Jonathan, and Carter Scholz, 'Receding Horizon', in *Kafka
   Americana* (W. W. Norton, 2001)

Levé, Edouard, *Autoportrait*, trans. Lorin Stein (Dalkey Archive, 2012)

— *Works*, trans. Jan Steyn (Dalkey Archive, 2014)

Lichtenberg, Georg Christoph, *Aphorisms & Letters*, trans. Franz
   Mautner and Henry Hatfield (Jonathan Cape, 1969)

McCarthy, Cormac, *The Road* (Picador, 2010)

Mansfield, Katherine, *Journal of Katherine Mansfield*, ed. J. Middleton
   Murry (Constable, 1967)

Markson, David, *This Is Not a Novel* (CB editions, 2012)

Mathews, Harry, *My Life in CIA* (Dalkey Archive, 2005)

— 'The Orchard', in *The Way Home: Selected Longer Prose* (Atlas Press,
   1999)

Miller, David, *Today* (Atlantic Books, 2012)

Molina, Antonio Muñoz, *Like a Fading Shadow*, trans. Camilo A.
   Ramirez (Serpent's Tail, 2018)

Muldoon, Paul, *One Thousand Things Worth Knowing* (Farrar, Straus and
   Giroux, 2015)

Nabokov, Vladimir, *Pnin* (Penguin, 1960)

— *Nikolai Gogol* (New Directions, 1961)

Oliver, Hermia, *Flaubert and an English Governess: The Quest for Juliet
   Herbert* (Clarendon Press, 1980)

Ozick, Cynthia, *Dictation* (Houghton Mifflin, 2008)

— 'T. S. Eliot at 101', in *What Henry James Knew* (Jonathan Cape, 1993)

Percy, Walker, *The Moviegoer* (1961; Methuen, 2004)

— 'The Man on the Train', in *The Message in the Bottle* (1975; St Martin's
   Press, 2000)

Pessoa, Fernando, *The Book of Disquiet*, trans. Margaret Jull Costa
   (Serpent's Tail, 1991)

Sante, Luc, *The Factory of Facts* (Granta, 1999)

Schwartz, Delmore, *In Dreams Begin Responsibilities* (New Directions, 1978)

Stach, Reiner, *Is That Kafka? 99 Finds*, trans. Kurt Beals (New Directions, 2016)

Starobinski, Jean, 'Pseudonymous Stendhal', in *The Living Eye*, trans. Arthur Goldhammer (Harvard UP, 1989)

Stendhal, *Memoirs of an Egotist*, trans. David Ellis (1832; Chatto & Windus, 1975)

— *The Red and the Black*, trans. Roger Gard (1830; Penguin Classics, 2002)

— *To the Happy Few: Selected Letters of Stendhal*, trans. Norman Cameron (John Lehman, 1952)

Stevenson, Robert Louis, *The Master of Ballantrae* (1889; Penguin Classics, 1996)

Tabucchi, Antonio, *Pereira Maintains*, trans. Patrick Creagh (Canongate, 2011)

Tonks, Rosemary, *Bedouin of the London Evening: Collected Poems* (Bloodaxe, 2016)

Vaughan, Dai, *Totes Meer* (Seren, 2003)

Williams, C. K., *Flesh and Blood* (Bloodaxe, 1988)

Williams, John, *Stoner* (1965; Vintage, 2013)

Wollstonecraft, Mary, *Letters Written in Sweden, Norway, and Denmark*, ed. Tone Brekke and Jon Mee (1796; OUP, 2009)

Woolf, Virginia, *Mr Bennett and Mrs Brown* (Hogarth Press, 1924)

Zambra, Alejandro, *Ways of Going Home*, trans. Megan McDowell (Granta, 2013)

— *Not to Read*, trans. Megan McDowell (Fitzcarraldo Editions, 2018)

.

INDEX

This is an index of things chatted about, not authors referenced.

acknowledgements 27-9

advice 21, 22-3, 61, 141

agents 21, 125, 175

anonymous 142, 175

awkwardness 7, 41, 43, 60, 73, 95, 96, 112, 171

bananas 36, 120

beards 74, 97, 115, 150

beggars 30, 38-9, 46

bicycles 13, 41, 45, 55, 68, 98-9, 157, 160

biographies (and memoirs) 6, 30, 49, 94, 112, 113, 115-16, 117

blurbs 44, 99

bookshelves 20, 39, 53, 55, 102

bonfires (and other fires) 8, 95, 158, 160, 166

childhood reading 14-15, 16, 32, 173

children 58, 79, 90, 92, 117, 121, 125, 150

cigarettes *see* smoking

classification 112, 144, 145

clichés 100, 162

cockroaches 11, 159

coffee *passim; see esp.* 119

coffee tables 108

cooking 54, 67

copy editors 145, 150

cover design 88, 90

creative writing 21, 22, 112

cricket 51, 147, 167

death 37, 69, 139, 151, 152-3, 162, 165, 167-8

death of the novel 118-19

description 45, 125-6

dictation 56, 93-4, 131

dogs 21, 70, 85, 112, 113, 147, 165, 169, 170

dreams 29, 50, 100-101, 174

dystopias 77-9, 124

eBooks 157

endings 71, 148, 152, 154-6, 162-3, 169, 170, 172

epigraphs 49-50

erotica 25, 112

failure 40, 53, 61, 70-71, 121

festivals 82

films 11, 28, 29, 30-31, 40, 78, 86, 87, 105, 116, 118, 140, 144, 154

genre 8-9, 97

golf 146-7

guns 9, 78, 144, 175

Hampstead novels 76-7, 81-2

happiness 80-81

hats 3, 20, 84, 113, 135, 136, 159, 160, 169

hitch-hiking 6, 144

holidays 49, 50-51, 103, 138, 172-3

hotels 4, 9, 30, 55, 89, 96, 101, 164

identity 10, 161

Ikea 53, 64

imprisonment 80, 90, 151, 165

interviews 5, 10, 67, 113, 140

jokes 11, 19, 22, 48, 122, 134, 156-7

justice 45, 87, 88, 111, 163, 170-71

left-handedness 30-31, 87

letters 31-2, 66-7, 149, 166

librarians 81, 130

libraries 14, 17, 32, 77, 108, 129, 153, 158, 164, 168, 173

long books 108, 118

magazines 25, 31, 55, 63, 64, 69-70, 87, 108, 126, 130, 150, 166, 170

metafiction 14, 104, 152

mirrors 102, 104, 105, 106

miscellaneous 163-6

modernism 68, 133-4, 160

money 5, 11, 31, 32, 39, 55, 76, 95, 111, 140

names of characters 64, 111

notebooks 63-4, 105-7

pen names 2, 3-4, 123, 17, 24, 25-7, 34-5, 43-4, 67, 96, 103, 117, 139

photographs 55-6, 91-2, 99, 130, 140-41, 143, 160, 174-5

plagiarism 129

plain style 66, 67

poetry 12, 22, 48, 69, 74-5, 80, 95, 120, 121, 123, 125, 168

porn 4, 16, 55, 112, 113, 114, 130

poshlust 33-4, 48, 78, 101

privilege 10, 101-2, 103, 128, 159

prizes 47, 66, 88, 98, 101, 117, 129, 165

pseudonyms *see* pen names

publishing 2, 57, 70, 71, 85, 86, 90, 95, 101, 107, 108-11, 121, 128, 145-6, 158

punctuality 41-2, 157

punctuation 41, 56, 87, 166, 171

rain 1, 6, 7, 11, 45, 51, 73, 83-4, 91, 94, 146, 150, 160-61

reading on public transport 58-9, 69, 75, 135

readings (and other author events) 73, 74, 81, 82

realism 39, 97, 105, 162

rejections 42, 109-10, 172

rereading 70, 71, 88, 89, 96, 172

reviews 12, 26, 33, 37-8, 97, 101, 113, 165

rubbish 19-20, 54, 141-2, 158

second-hand bookshops 18-19, 139, 161

self-loathing 36, 45, 63, 121; *see also* waste

sentimentality (and schmaltz) 78, 79, 152-3

sex 15, 25, 61, 64-6, 68, 90, 98, 104, 114-15, 126, 127, 132, 140, 163

shoes 13, 60, 159

shoplifting 82

shop talk 47, 62

signed copies 13, 95, 139

silence 7, 44, 61, 72, 73, 74, 129,
    138, 140, 146-7, 152
smoking 5, 13, 30, 38, 39, 48, 51,
    62, 90, 91, 95, 146, 148, 160,
    168-9
social media 12, 31, 37, 101, 114,
    121
sport 51-2; *see also* cricket; golf
statistics 43, 52, 110
stupidity 8, 31, 34
throwing away 141, 142, 150
titles 9-10, 101, 149; of books
    never written 62
toilets 20, 54, 82-3, 103, 104, 105

tossing a coin 83
transcribers 57-8, 131-3, 93-4,
    132, 135
translation 37, 39, 94, 142-3, 167
umbrellas 1, 12, 15, 58, 83-4,
    135-6, 137-9, 159, 160, 169
waste 121-5
work 17, 22-3, 24, 38, 39, 56, 73,
    113, 128, 140, 153, 156, 172,
    175
work in progress 111, 127
writers' rooms 55-6
writing in cafés 140
Young Adults 15, 125

editions

Founded in 2007, CB editions publishes chiefly short
fiction and poetry, including work in translation.
Books can be ordered from www.cbeditions.com.